SEMICONDUCTOR MONOGRAPHS

# SEMICONDUCTOR PARTICLE DETECTORS

# SEMICONDUCTOR MONOGRAPHS

*General Editor*
C. A. HOGARTH, Ph.D., F.Inst.P.

PREPARATION OF SINGLE CRYSTALS

OPTICAL PROPERTIES OF SEMI-CONDUCTORS

FLUCTUATION PHENOMENA IN
SEMI-CONDUCTORS

THE HALL EFFECT AND RELATED
PHENOMENA

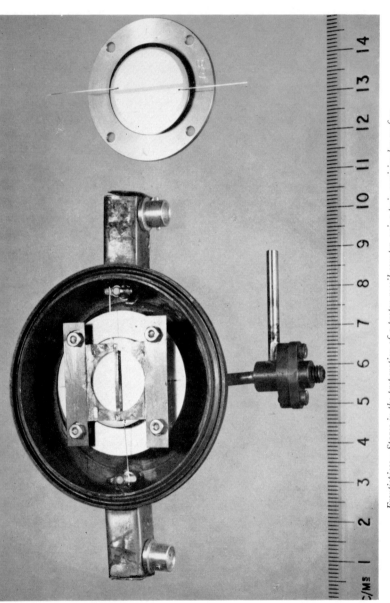

*Frontispiece—Stages in the preparation of a proton recoil counter, using twin semicircular surface barrier detectors made from a single slice of silicon*

# SEMICONDUCTOR
# PARTICLE DETECTORS

J. M. TAYLOR

B.Sc., M.Sc., A.F.R.Ae.Soc.

LONDON

BUTTERWORTHS

1963

| | |
|---|---|
| *ENGLAND:* | BUTTERWORTH & CO. (PUBLISHERS) LTD.<br>LONDON: 88 Kingsway, W.C.2 |
| *AFRICA:* | BUTTERWORTH & CO. (AFRICA) LTD.<br>DURBAN: 33/35 Beach Grove |
| *AUSTRALIA:* | BUTTERWORTH & CO. (AUSTRALIA) LTD.<br>SYDNEY: 6/8 O'Connell Street<br>MELBOURNE: 473 Bourke Street<br>BRISBANE: 240 Queen Street |
| *CANADA:* | BUTTERWORTH & CO. (CANADA) LTD.<br>TORONTO: 1367 Danforth Avenue, 6 |
| *NEW ZEALAND:* | BUTTERWORTH & CO. (NEW ZEALAND) LTD.<br>WELLINGTON: 49/51 Ballance Street<br>AUCKLAND: 35 High Street |
| *U.S.A.:* | BUTTERWORTH INC.<br>WASHINGTON, D.C.: 7235 Wisconsin Avenue, 14 |

Suggested U.D.C. Number 539.12.074:537.311.33

*Printed in Great Britain by*
*Spottiswoode, Ballantyne and Co. Ltd.*
*London and Colchester*

# FOREWORD

THE fields of physics being most actively investigated and gainfully applied are solid-state and nuclear physics. In particular, the transport and optical properties of semiconductors have received particular attention in laboratories all over the world and these properties have been exploited in many semiconductor devices such as $p$–$n$ junction rectifiers, transistors, and photoconductive detectors. The use of solids, particularly semiconductors in the detection of nucleons, is an interesting example of a useful interaction between the above two fields of physics in which the incident nuclear particle causes the current flowing in the device to increase and thus detect and possibly count it. This interaction may be contrasted with another, namely radiation damage, in which high doses of nucleons cause permanent and sometimes catastrophic damage to solid materials.

The serious development of semiconductor particle detectors has taken place in the past ten years and Colonel Taylor's book provides a complete account of the theory and practice of the subject at the present time. The book must, to some extent, be regarded as a status report, in view of the rapid development of the subject all over the world. Nevertheless, the book should be of value to workers in a specialized corner of the field by describing the subject in a wider sense. In view of the fact that the book may be used by nuclear physicists the introductory account of semiconductor physics is rather longer than might be expected, so that the work is complete in itself. Readers who require a fuller introduction to the subject should consult companion volumes by Dr. E. H. Putley on *The Hall Effect and Related Phenomena* and by Dr. T. S. Moss on *Optical Properties of Semiconductors*.

C. A. HOGARTH

# CONTENTS

## CONTENTS

# INTRODUCTION

METHODS of particle detection are of supreme importance for nearly all experimental work in the fields of atomic and nuclear physics, and it is, therefore, of great interest that in the last few years most encouraging results have been obtained with entirely new techniques using semiconductors. The development of these detectors is still in its infancy. Although the possibilities were demonstrated in an experiment by McKay[1] in 1949, and Walter *et al.*[2] produced a number of germanium surface barrier counters in 1956–58, development was delayed for some years by lack of satisfactory materials. Interest in the subject was enormously stimulated in the late 1950s, when high resistivity, single crystal silicon of *P*-type first became available. It was then possible to make junction counters which would operate well at ambient temperatures. Subsequently, *N*-type silicon of comparable purity and perfection has been produced.

Since 1959 there has been a considerable research effort in this field and the scientific literature is already quite extensive. The detectors are no longer just laboratory-produced experimental models but are available commercially and their use in particle experiments is rapidly becoming a commonplace. There seems to be no doubt that the speed of development will be sustained over the next few years and that these devices will make a contribution to experimental particle physics at least as important as that already made by the introduction of the scintillation counter.

The particular virtues of semiconductor detection are most valuable in applications to the spectrometry of charged particles. They are used in conjunction with an amplifier and a pulse height analyser, and by means of this relatively cheap assembly very good particle energy spectra may be obtained. Individual counters differ in their properties over quite a wide range and their manufacture is not yet sufficiently controlled to enable them to be produced to a specification. However, it is not difficult to obtain, by selection, counters which have the following characteristics with charged particles of mass in the region 1 to 4 units and energy 4 to 8 MeV:

(a) A fast pulse rise, the entire leading edge being developed within about 5 nsec;
(b) No apparent dead time;
(c) Linearity with particle energy, regardless of the nature of the particle;

(d) Detection efficiency apparently 100 per cent, i.e. any charged particle of adequate mass and energy entering the sensitive volume will be detected;

(e) Energy resolution of 0·4 per cent (f.w.h.m.†) or better;

(f) High stability in time and under high counting rates;

(g) Ability to operate through a moderate background of gamma, beta or neutron radiation.

Such counters would, in fact, have a satisfactory response to heavier particles and over a much wider range of energy (from approximately 50 keV for mass 1, up to several hundred MeV for fission fragments) but there may be some deterioration in energy resolution, pulse rise time and other factors.

A counter with the properties described above would have an aperture of a few mm². Smaller ones, down to 1 mm² or less, can easily be made and the counter could then have a total volume of only 1mm³. At the expense of some loss in energy resolution, apertures of 6 cm² can be obtained, and larger ones are likely to be made in the near future. For specific purposes, and with a little trouble, one or more of the above attributes may be improved at the expense of others. For example, a pulse rise time less than 1 nsec appears possible, subject to an amplifying system which would realize this in practice; or, by the use of a different type of counter, the range of linearity with energy may be extended. Counters with a potentially useful response to beta, gamma, and neutron radiation can also be made.

The combination of good energy resolution with fast rise time opens up new fields in particle selection, while the small size and consistently good linearity and efficiency facilitate scattering experiments and the measurement of reaction cross-sections. Limitations lie in the fact that the detectors give a signal of only a few millivolts and considerable amplification is needed. This can be achieved, but only at the expense of other properties. Although the small size of the counters is an advantage in many applications, it results in rather poor efficiency for gamma and beta radiations. There are difficulties in obtaining a large sensitive volume which have yet to be overcome. All types so far developed are sensitive to high temperatures and some require cooling to 100° K or less to obtain good results. All have a limited life under strong radiation with heavy particles.

A description is given in this book of the physics of semiconductor detectors, the factors governing their properties and the methods of manufacture and employment. It has been considered necessary to

† See Appendix D.

include two chapters (1 and 3) on those aspects of solid state physics which are most relevant. Although this information is obtainable from a number of textbooks, such works are written with a view to other applications and do not, in general, give an adequate account of the particular aspects most relevant to particle detectors. These chapters have been written solely to state the background to particle detection problems; complications have been omitted where possible and the limited mathematical treatment is sometimes non-rigorous.

## REFERENCES

[1] McKay, K. G., *Phys. Rev.* 76 (1949) 1537
[2] Walter, F. J., Dabbs, J. W. T., Roberts, L. D. and Wright, H. W., *O.R.N.L. Rep.* CF 58-11-99 (1958)

# LIST OF SYMBOLS

$A$    The cross-section or aperture of a counter.

$C$    Capacitance.

$D$    Diffusion coefficient of carriers.

$E$    Energy, or energy level; usually with a suffix.

$\epsilon$    Dielectric constant.

$F$    Electric field strength.

$f$    The Fermi function, also used as a suffix to indicate the Fermi level, '$E_f$'.

$g$    Generation rate of a carrier or carrier pairs.

$h$    Planck's constant.

$I$    Electric current.

$i$    Used as a suffix to signify 'intrinsic'.

$k$    Boltzmann's constant.

$L$    Diffusion length of a carrier.

$m$    Effective mass of a carrier.

$\mu$    Mobility of a carrier.

$N$    Net concentration of donor centres ($N_D$) or acceptor centres ($N_A$). Also used to indicate the nature of extrinsic conductivity, '$N$-type'.

$n$    Concentration of electron carriers, or concentration of an unspecified carrier. Also used as a suffix to indicate the nature of a carrier, e.g. '$\mu_n$'.

$P$    Used to indicate the nature of extrinsic conductivity, '$P$-type'.

$p$    Concentration of hole carriers. Also used as a suffix to indicate the nature of a carrier, e.g. '$\mu_p$'.

$Q$    The equilibrium potential acting across a $P$–$N$ junction in the absence of applied bias.

$q$    The electron charge.

$\rho$    Electrical resistivity.

$T$    Temperature, always in degrees Kelvin.

$t$    Time.

$t_c$    Collecting time of excess carriers.

$\tau$    Carrier lifetime, usually with suffix, $n$ or $p$, which indicates the carrier concerned.

$V$    An electrical potential, usually the reverse bias applied across a junction.

$W$    Barrier depth in a $P.I.N.$ counter.

$X$    Barrier depth in a barrier layer counter.

# RELEVANT PROPERTIES OF SEMICONDUCTORS

## 1.1 Definition of a Semiconductor

It is useful to begin by defining, as far as possible, what is meant by the term 'semiconductor'. The following data[1] helps to clarify this, and other characteristics of these materials emerge later:

Conductors . . . resistivity of the order $10^{-5}\ \Omega$ cm
Semiconductors . . resistivity $10^{-2}$ to $10^9\ \Omega$ cm
Insulators . . . resistivity $10^{14}$ to $10^{22}\ \Omega$ cm

It should be understood that the figures quoted are not rigid limits, but the conductivities of solids at ambient temperatures are strongly grouped in these zones. Semiconductors are less numerous than the other two classes.

## 1.2 The Band Theory of Solids

The development of a satisfactory theory of electrical conduction in solids is a consequence of the introduction of quantum mechanical methods. The differences in conductivity depend on the fact that electrons within the material exist in certain well-defined energy states and can only gain or lose energy by transition from one state to another. For conduction to occur the random motion of some of the electrons must have, superimposed upon it, a component in the direction of the applied field. This additional motion involves the acquisition of increased energy and can therefore occur only if suitable closely spaced energy levels exist. Moreover, because of the exclusion principle, electron transitions to higher levels can only occur if the higher levels are not already occupied. For the purpose of this study it will suffice to consider the energy levels within a single crystal.

If two atoms of the same element are in close proximity, so that they form one quantum mechanical system, the energy levels of the various electronic shells must undergo some modification, otherwise pairs of electrons would be in identical quantum states, and the exclusion principle would be violated. In fact, each energy level splits into two very close levels, and the electrons originally occupying two identical levels in separate systems now occupy two slightly different levels in the same system. If further atoms are added the process of level-splitting continues, and in a crystal, with atoms disposed in an ordered lattice, each atomic energy level is replaced by a band of levels, closely spaced. This process is illustrated graphically in *Figure 1.1*, which relates to a metal of low atomic number, such as sodium or magnesium. The quantity *r*, plotted on the horizontal axis is the distance between atoms, and it is seen that as this decreases the well-defined electron energy levels of the isolated atoms are replaced by

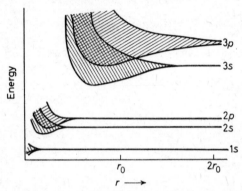

*Figure 1.1. The effect of close atomic spacing on the energy
levels in a crystal*

(D. Woolridge, A. J. Ahearn and J. A. Burton, *Phys. Rev.* 71 (1947) 913,
by courtesy of the American Physical Society)

wide bands. As might be expected, the outer electron shells are first affected and the innermost shells remain isolated systems down to very small values of *r*. The distance $r_0$ is the atomic spacing in the crystalline solid under normal conditions and it is seen that the 3*s* and 3*p* bands are merged, forming a single band of exceptional width. Another consequence of the close atomic spacing is shown in *Figure 1.2*. The ogival curves indicate the potential energy of an electron in relation to its distance from successive nuclei and the spaces between them represent the familiar concept of 'energy wells' within which the atomic electrons are normally confined. It is seen that electrons in the 2*p* band and below are still restricted to the vicinity of the nuclei, as for widely separated atoms. However, the coulomb field of each atomic core is partly neutralized by those of adjacent cores, and consequently the tops of the potential wells, i.e. the maxima of the ogival curves, are much below the arbitrary energy zero of an electron in free space. Electrons in the 3*s* band and higher bands have energies

2

greater than this and are therefore not bound to any particular nucleus. In quantum mechanical terms, the modulus of the wave function for an electron in one of the higher energy bands has appreciable values over the whole crystal. Furthermore, ignoring surface effects, the wave function repeats itself in each unit cell of the lattice, so that the electron is equally likely to be found in any one of them. Electrons occupying levels in these upper bands are in a state of random motion and are confined only by the boundaries of the crystal; they are described as 'free electrons' and they constitute the 'electron gas' which is a necessary pre-requisite for conduction.

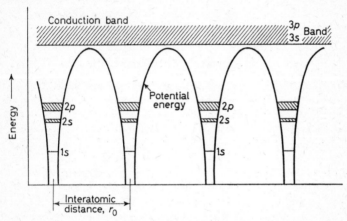

*Figure 1.2. Schematic diagram of the band structure of metallic magnesium*

Solids which contain an electron gas will still be non-conductors if the energy bands occupied by the free electrons are completely filled. This is because transitions are forbidden by the exclusion principle and none of the electrons can acquire the necessary additional energy. It has already been noted that in metallic magnesium the $3s$ and $3p$ bands unite, and as the $3p$ levels are empty in the normal state of this atom the double band resulting is by no means full. If there are $n$ atoms in the crystal there will be $2n$ quantum states derived from the $3s$ shell plus $6n$ states from the $3p$ shell; but there will only be $2n$ electrons from the $3s$ shell. It is therefore evident that these electrons, derived from the outer shell of the atomic structure, are 'free' and also enjoy an environment in which there are plenty of closely spaced, unoccupied energy levels. They can therefore acquire small increments of energy, up to the limit imposed by the top of the band, and can be accelerated by an applied electric field. These electrons are responsible for conduction and the energy band they occupy (which is only partly filled) is termed the 'conduction band'. It may be noted here that, in metals, the concentration of conduction electrons is of the order $10^{22}/cm^3$.

The fact that magnesium is a conductor is primarily due to the overlap of the $3s$ and $3p$ bands; consider what would happen if these two bands were separated from each other by an appreciable gap, so that electrons could not effect transitions from one to the other. Referring to *Figure 1.1*, this structure would arise if the atomic spacing were somewhat greater, about $1 \cdot 3r_0$. This type of band structure is typical of insulators and is one reason for the absence of conductivity; many 'free' electrons are present, but they occupy filled energy bands and cannot respond to any applied field.

## 1.3  INTRINSIC SEMICONDUCTORS

In certain substances (e.g. silicon, germanium) the band structure of the crystal is qualitatively the same as that of an insulator (described above) but the uppermost filled band is separated from a higher empty band by only a small forbidden zone. These substances are insulators at low temperatures but at higher temperatures some of the electrons from the top of the uppermost filled band acquire sufficient thermal energy to cross the small forbidden zone into the empty band above. These electrons are then able to conduct, and the band they now occupy is termed the 'conduction band'. The band below this, which is filled at zero temperature, is termed the 'valence band' and the forbidden zone between them is the 'energy gap' (*Figure 1.3*). The minimum energy increment needed for an electron to enter the conduction band is denoted by '$E_G$' and its value, in semiconductors, ranges from about 0·1 to 3 eV.

Values of $E_G$ for a number of semiconductors are given in Appendix A.

It has already been explained that electrons in the conduction band are able to respond to an electric field and can therefore carry current. They are termed 'electron carriers' or, if no confusion is likely to arise, simply 'electrons'. It is also necessary to appreciate that the removal of electrons from the valence band is, in itself, a process leading to conduction, because the vacancies created in the band do allow some electrons to acquire energy from an applied field. It is common practice to think of valence band conduction as a process in which positive charges are conveyed by the 'holes' in the otherwise filled band.

The idea that a vacant energy level in the valence band can be

4

equivalent to a positive charge carrier is difficult to accept intellectually, because an energy level does not, of course, have any location in Cartesian space. Nevertheless, this concept is extremely useful in developing an understanding of the behaviour of semiconductors and its success can be explained by quantum mechanical theory. A brief account of this theory, which serves as an introduction to a more advanced study of the subject, is given by Cusack[2]. For the present purpose it will suffice to accept the undoubted fact that in semiconductors there are two types of charge carrier, electrons and holes,

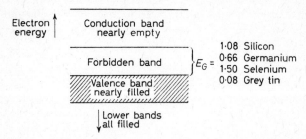

Figure 1.3. Valence and conduction bands in group IV elements: $E_G$ values are in electron volts and apply to 300° K

and that in the case of an ideal intrinsic semiconductor they are created simultaneously in equal numbers.

The entry of electrons into the conduction band is, of course, a reversible process and when the crystal is in its normal condition of dynamic equilibrium the rate of 'recombination' of electrons and holes is equal to the rate of generation. The latter is governed by the temperature and the former, being subject to the law of mass action, is governed by the concentration of electrons and holes. The concentration of carriers is therefore strongly temperature dependent and is given approximately by the equation

$$n = p = 10^{19} . \exp\left(-\frac{E_G}{2kT}\right) \qquad \dots (1.1)$$

where $n$ is the electron concentration (per cm$^3$) in the conduction band and $p$ is the hole concentration in the valence band; $k$ is Boltzmann's constant and $T$ the absolute temperature. At room temperature $kT$ is about 0·026 eV, so the carrier concentration is many orders of magnitude below the figure $10^{22}$ applicable to metallic conductors. If, for example, $E_G$ is 1 eV, the concentration of each carrier is roughly $2 \times 10^{10}$/cm$^3$ at room temperature. This very much lower concentration of charge carriers, and its temperature dependence, are primarily responsible for the difference between the electrical properties of a semiconductor and those of a metal.

## 1.4   EXTRINSIC, OR IMPURITY SEMICONDUCTORS

It is possible for an electron to reach the conduction band without necessarily originating in the valence band. This can happen as the result of an impurity in the crystal, which liberates electrons into the conduction band without leaving corresponding holes in the valence band. Consider the case of four-valent germanium 'doped' with an element of group V, such as arsenic. The arsenic atoms are 'substitutional' impurities (they occupy positions in the lattice normally

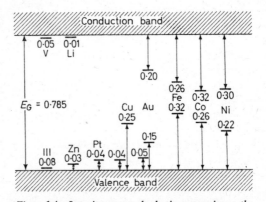

Figure 1.4. Impurity energy levels in germanium; the levels marked III, V, stand for group III and group V elements; the arrows show the possible transitions

(Proceedings of Photoconductivity Conference, 1954, by courtesy of Wiley, New York)

occupied by an atom of germanium) and four electrons from each atom enter the valence band of the crystal. The fifth arsenic electron, however, at low temperatures remains loosely bound to its parent atomic core; this is a consequence of the fact that the nucleus has a slightly stronger coulomb field than its neighbours. In quantum mechanical terms, the fifth electron occupies a state whose wave-function is localized. The energy level of this state is termed the 'impurity level', and it can be shown[1] that it lies near the top of the energy gap of the crystal band structure (see *Figure 1.4*).

Let the impurity level be $E_D$ electron volts below the conduction band, where $E_D \ll E_G$. The situation is now somewhat similar to that of an intrinsic semiconductor with a much reduced energy gap, and as the temperature rises electrons from the impurity atoms acquire enough energy to enter the conduction band. The difference is, however, that the hole left by the electron is not mobile and is not a current carrier. It is, of course, possible for an electron from the valence band to occupy the local energy level and leave a new, conducting hole behind it. However, since $E_D$ is substantially less than $E_G$, the former process is much more probable and the impurity, therefore, adds many conduction electrons to the system but very few conducting holes. Impurity atoms which have this effect are termed 'donors'; their impurity levels are termed 'donor levels', and the resulting crystal (having an excess of negative carriers) is described as an '$N$'-type semiconductor. When, in an 'extrinsic' semiconductor, the carrier concentrations are unequal the terms 'majority carriers' and 'minority carriers' are frequently used.

It can also happen that an impurity creates holes in the valence band without releasing a corresponding number of electrons into the conduction band. This happens, for example, with a tri-valent element such as phosphorus in a crystal of silicon. Each phosphorus atom, lacking a valence bond to complete the lattice, provides a hole of fixed location, which may be filled by an electron acquiring energy slightly above that of the top of the valence band. At normal temperatures nearly all these fixed impurity levels are occupied by electrons from the valence band, and this results in a semiconductor with an excess of holes, described as '$P$-type' (having positive carriers). The impurity is described as an 'acceptor' and the impurity levels are 'acceptor levels'. The energy gap of germanium is illustrated in *Figure 1.4*, with some impurity levels and the respective values of $E_D$ and $E_A$; the latter is measured positively from the top of the valence band.

The description of impurity semiconduction given above is necessarily brief and incomplete. The only requirement is that there should be fixed points or centres in the lattice which can readily donate electrons to the conduction band or accept electrons from the valence band. The centres may arise from impurity atoms, substitutional or interstitial, or from other lattice defects such as vacant sites or interstitial atoms of the pure material. As shown in *Figure 1.4*, there are some impurities which produce centres at more than one energy level. The subject is further complicated by the fact that crystals always have both donor and acceptor impurities or defects in them and the nature of the semiconductivity ($P$ or $N$) is determined by the one which is present in excess. The donor and acceptor defects neutralize each other. If the concentration of donors, $N_D$, exceeds that of acceptors, $N_A$, the semiconductor will be an $N$-type with approximately $N_D$–$N_A$ effective donors per cubic centimetre. This process is termed 'compensation' and enables a $P$-type crystal to be converted to $N$-type by addition of a donor impurity in excess of the acceptor already present, and vice versa. The symbols '$N_D$' and '$N_A$' used above to represent total impurity concentrations, are normally used to represent the net donor or net acceptor concentrations, respectively. Except where otherwise stated they will be used in the latter sense in this book.

A very small amount of impurity (one part in $10^6$ or $10^7$) gives appreciable extrinsic conductivity and the vast majority of semi-conductors cannot be made intrinsic, or even nearly so, purely by refining. It can happen in the refining of silicon that an approach to intrinsic resistivity is obtained by compensation but, at present, this is more or less accidental, unless special measures are adopted which will be described later in this section, and in Chapter 2, sections 5 and 6. Germanium is rather more amenable in this respect, partly because it can be obtained in a somewhat higher state of purity but mainly because the intrinsic conductivity is relatively high at ambient temperatures, and the extrinsic conductivity is less apparent. A large number of semiconductors, particularly among the ionic crystals (e.g. zinc oxide and the alkali halides) would more properly be classed as insulators if they were pure and perfect, and showed only extrinsic conductivity. When a semiconducting material is refined it usually happens that one particular impurity most resists removal and this determines whether the product is $P$- or $N$-type. In silicon, for example, the residual impurity is boron, which is an acceptor. Samples of the opposite type are then obtained by deliberate over-compensation.

It should perhaps be emphasized that the terms 'donor' and 'acceptor' are usually applied only to impurities which create localized quantum states close to the edges of the forbidden zone (0·2 eV, or less) and which therefore have a strong effect on the number of carriers. In such cases it normally happens, at ambient temperatures and even much below ambient, that the impurity levels are almost completely ionized. Furthermore, over a considerable range of temperature, the effect of such impurities so considerably dominates the intrinsic conductivity that it is reasonably accurate to neglect the latter. The conduction in an $N$-type semiconductor is, therefore, almost entirely due to a concentration, $N_D$ of carrier electrons. Similarly, in a $P$-type crystal, it is normally valid to assume that the conductivity is entirely due to a concentration of holes equal to the net concentration of acceptors.

Impurities which create quantum states near the middle of the forbidden zone do, in fact, influence the carrier concentrations, and some of their effects will be mentioned later. Although they cannot properly be regarded as donors or acceptors their presence is very relevant to the question of compensation. For example, gold in silicon produces vacant levels deep in the energy gap and these will neutralize donor centres, but not on a one-for-one basis. This effect, reported by Collins et al.[3] can be utilized to produce silicon of nearly intrinsic resistivity and is described in a little more detail in Chapter 2, sections 5 and 6.

The equilibrium condition in a semiconductor (the values of $n$ and $p$, in particular) is a dynamic equilibrium involving a number of processes which will be discussed in more detail in Chapter 1.9. The various processes which create carriers are all reversible and under equilibrium conditions each process and its converse occurs with equal frequency (this is the 'principle of detailed balancing'[4]). In an intrinsic semiconductor at equilibrium the creation of electrons and holes is balanced by their recombination at an equal rate. In an extrinsic semiconductor the donor and acceptor processes are added. The ultimate fate of a hole is always its recombination with an electron and vice versa. Sometimes both are mobile (direct recombination); in other cases one or other is immobile, at a localized quantum state.

## 1.5 THE FERMI LEVEL

Electrons in a solid obey Fermi Dirac statistics, according to which the probability that a particular energy level will be filled is given by the Fermi function:

$$f = \frac{1}{1 + e^{(E - E_f)/kT}} \qquad \ldots (1.2)$$

In this expression, $k$ is Boltzmann's constant, $T$ is the absolute temperature and $E$ is the energy of the particular quantum state concerned; $E_f$ is a parameter, depending on the properties of the system, whose magnitude governs the value of $E$ at which $f = \frac{1}{2}$. The significance of $E_f$ is best appreciated by considering the shape of the function for various values of $T$. This is illustrated in *Figure 1.5*.

At all temperatures, $f$ is unity for low values of $E$ ($E_f - E \gg kT$) and zero at high values, but the transition between these extremes is very sharp when the temperature is low and relatively gradual for high temperatures. (In fact, the value of $E_f$ is slightly temperature-dependent but the effect is negligible for the present purpose.) $E_f$ is termed the 'Fermi level' and it can readily be seen that it measures the extent to which the system is filled with electrons. If more electrons are added, $E_f$ will increase. If more quantum states are added, in the region below $E_f$, the effective capacity of the system is increased and $E_f$ will fall.

The concept of the Fermi function [eqn. (1.2)] is easily understood for the case of a metal, where the Fermi level is within a wide conduction band. However, the concept is equally applicable even when the Fermi level falls within a forbidden zone, or energy gap. It is helpful to regard the forbidden zone, not as a region in which there are no energy levels, but as a region containing only a small concentration

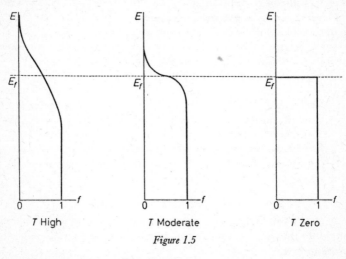

*Figure 1.5*

of levels. The Fermi function then applies to these levels and gives the probability that they are occupied, in just the same way as it applies to levels within the valence and conduction bands. Furthermore, at zero temperature the valence band is full and the conduction band is empty, it therefore follows that the Fermi level must lie somewhere in the energy gap.

It is shown in most of the standard works on this subject that, in the case of an intrinsic semiconductor, the Fermi level lies near the centre of the forbidden zone. The Fermi function, the energy gap, and the density of states function are illustrated in the schematic diagram of *Figure 1.6*, for the case of an intrinsic semiconductor at moderate temperatures. It is seen that the conductivity arises from the fact that the tail of the Fermi function straddles the forbidden zone, thereby giving a finite probability that a level near the bottom of the conduction band will be filled and a finite probability that a level near the top of the valence band will be empty. Comparison with *Figure 1.5* shows how the carrier concentrations change with temperature.

10

The addition of donor impurities to an otherwise intrinsic crystal has the effect of (*a*) increasing the number of electrons in the system; (*b*) increasing the number of states available in the upper part of the energy gap. The donor atoms therefore raise the Fermi level, *n* increases and *p* is reduced. However, since electrons have been added to the system, the former effect is dominant and the total carrier concentration is increased. If the crystal is now cooled to zero temperature the electrons fill the donor levels and leave the conduction band empty. Consequently, the Fermi level now lies between the donor level and the conduction band. With increasing temperature it soon falls below the donor level (temperature dependence is appreciable

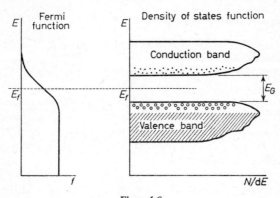

*Figure 1.6*

in an extrinsic conductor) and at high temperatures again approaches the middle of the gap. At all temperatures, and for all values of $N_D$, it remains within the energy gap. The material therefore remains a semiconductor, having zero conductivity at zero temperature.

The presence of acceptor atoms creates additional levels below the Fermi level, but does not add electrons. The effect is therefore precisely the converse of that of donors. The Fermi level falls, but remains within the energy gap; the concentration of holes is increased and that of electrons is reduced.

It is now apparent that the difference between an intrinsic, an *N*- and a *P*-type semiconductor is best defined in terms of the Fermi level and its position in the energy gap. The process of compensation, too, is better understood in relation to its effect on the Fermi level. It should be noted that the conductivity is not solely determined by the Fermi level. Because of the difference in mobility† between electrons

† See 1.7.

and holes, the minimum of conductivity for silicon is slightly lower than the intrinsic conductivity and occurs with a material that is slightly $P$-type.

Referring again to eqn. (1.2), the probability that a level near the bottom of the conduction band will contain an electron is determined by the difference between its energy and that of the Fermi level $(E-E_f)$. If this is large compared with $kT$, the additive unit in the denominator may be neglected. In this case,

$$f = e^{-(E-E_f)/kT}$$
$$= e^{E_f/kT} . e^{-E/kT}$$
$$= A . e^{-E/kT}$$

where A is a constant.

This distribution function is identical in form with that for the classical theory of an electron gas, the Maxwell–Boltzmann distribution. In semiconductor crystals at ambient temperatures and below, the above approximation is often valid, and consequently the carriers have an energy distribution of the Maxwell–Boltzmann form. Because of this such specimens are termed 'classical' semiconductors. The approximation is not valid in heavily doped material where the Fermi level is very close to the conduction band, and the crystal is then described as 'degenerate'.

To take a specific example, the quantity $kT$ at 300°K is 0·026 eV; the energy gap for silicon is 1·08 eV. Assume that in a silicon crystal the Fermi level is only 0·1 $E_G$ below the conduction band, a condition which would correspond to very heavy doping and would give a resistivity less than 0·1 $\Omega$ cm. For any level in the conduction band,

$$E-E_f > 4\,kT$$

therefore,

$$e^{E-E_f/kT} > e^4 > 54$$

It is, therefore, reasonably accurate in this case to neglect the unit in the denominator of eqn. (1.2), the error being less than 2 per cent, and the specimen could still be described as 'classical'.

A similar argument can be applied to the function $(1-f)$, the probability that a level will be unoccupied. It is then found convenient to adopt a convention for the energy of a hole, by which the energy increases positively as the electron energy level concerned falls lower. This energy is therefore measured downwards on the reference axes of *Figure 1.6*, from some convenient arbitrary zero, such as the top of the valence band. It is found that the holes also obey Boltzmann statistics, except in very heavily doped crystal.

The basic crystal used in making semiconductor detectors of existing types is always 'classical' and would not be much use for the purpose otherwise. Some parts of the crystals are afterwards heavily doped and may become degenerate. For classical crystal, it can be shown that if there are $n$ carriers per $cm^3$ the number having energy exceeding a certain level $E_B$ is given by

$$n' = n \cdot e^{-E_B/kT} \qquad \ldots (1.3)$$

where $E_B$ is measured from the bottom of the conduction band or the top of the valence band, as appropriate.

## 1.6 CARRIER CONCENTRATIONS

It follows from the previous section that in any classical semiconductor, where Maxwell–Boltzmann statistics apply, the concentration of electron carriers, $n$, is given by a law of the form

$$n = C_n \cdot e^{-E_n/kT}$$

where $E_n$ is the energy difference between the Fermi level and the bottom of the conduction band, and $C_n$ is a constant. It can also be shown that the concentration of holes obeys a similar law,

$$p = C_p \cdot e^{-E_p/kT}$$

where $E_p$ is the energy difference (regarded as positive) between the Fermi level and the top of the valence band. From this the product,

$$n \cdot p = C_n \cdot C_p e^{-(E_n + E_p)/kT}$$
$$\cdot \quad = C_n \cdot C_p e^{-E_G/kT}$$

The product of the two carrier concentrations is therefore a constant, regardless of the position of the Fermi level. This is purely a consequence of Maxwell–Boltzmann statistics and applies, in a given material, whether it is intrinsic, $N$-type or $P$-type, good crystal or poor, provided it can be correctly described as 'classical'. A more rigorous treatment of this subject is given by Cusack[2] and by Ehrenberg[5], where it is shown that

$$n \cdot p = n_i^2 = N_n \cdot N_p \cdot e^{-E_G/kT} \qquad \ldots (1.4)$$

where
$$N_n = 2\left(\frac{2\pi m_n kT}{h}\right)^{\frac{3}{2}}$$

and
$$N_p = 2\left(\frac{2\pi m_p kT}{h}\right)^{\frac{3}{2}}$$

$h$ is Planck's constant and $m_n$, $m_p$ are the 'effective masses' of the electrons and holes respectively. The effective mass of a carrier differs considerably from the actual electronic mass and is really a property of the crystal. It is not usually the same for electrons and holes, even in the same crystal.

The quantity '$n_i$' is the concentration of either carrier in the intrinsic crystal and is an important parameter of a semiconductor. It is, of course, strongly temperature-dependent.

An important consequence of this law is the fact, already noted in connexion with the Fermi level, that doping a crystal not only increases the concentration of one type of carrier but also diminishes the concentration of the other. In practical cases the suppression of minority carriers is considerable. In $N$-type silicon of resistivity 1,000 $\Omega$ cm at ambient temperature, the concentration of electrons is about $5 \times 10^{12}/\text{cm}^3$; $n_i$ is about $1 \cdot 3 \times 10^{10}$. The concentration of holes is

$$p = \frac{n_i^2}{n} = \frac{1 \cdot 69 \times 10^{20}}{5 \times 10^{12}}$$

$$= 3 \cdot 4 \times 10^7$$

nearly three orders of magnitude below the intrinsic level. The total carrier concentration is, for all practical purposes, that of the electrons and is two orders of magnitude above the intrinsic level.

## 1.7 CARRIER MOBILITY

The conductivity of a solid is largely determined by the carrier concentration, but a factor of almost equal importance is the speed with which the carriers move under the influence of an applied electric field. At normal temperatures the electrons in the conduction band are subject to constant interaction with the thermal vibrations of the crystal lattice, and are therefore in a state of random motion similar to the well-known Brownian motion of fluid molecules. Any systematic motion of the electrons due to an applied field is super-imposed on the random motion and is described as the 'drift velocity'. At normal temperatures the drift velocity is substantially smaller than the mean thermal velocity and is proportional to field strength up to about $10^3$ V/cm. The constant of proportionality is termed 'mobility' and is defined by the equation

$$\mu = v_d/F \, (\text{cm}^2/\text{V sec}) \qquad \ldots (1.5)$$

Mobility can be defined in various ways, depending on the method of measurement and the numerical values quoted differ accordingly. As used here, the word 'mobility' always refers to the 'drift mobility', and is related to the drift velocity by eqn. (1.5). Values of carrier mobility for some semiconductors are given in Appendix A.

The thermal agitation of the electrons mentioned above is termed 'lattice scattering' and is the main factor limiting their motion under an applied field. Consequently, mobility is quite strongly temperature dependent and can rise to very high values in crystals cooled, for example, in liquid nitrogen. The law of temperature dependence is illustrated diagrammatically in *Figure 1.7*. If a semiconductor crystal

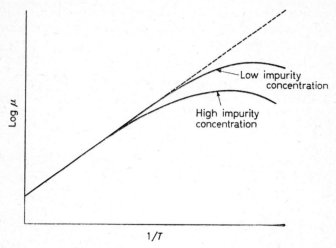

*Figure 1.7. Temperature dependence of carrier mobility*

were really pure and perfect, $\log \mu$ would be linear with the reciprocal of temperature, but even very small amounts of impurities have a considerable effect. As the temperature falls 'impurity scattering' increases and there is usually an optimum temperature for maximum mobility.

The concept of mobility is not restricted to electrons, but applies equally to holes. In the same material at a given temperature hole mobilities are usually less than those of electrons.

For particle detection the only semiconductors so far used extensively are silicon and germanium. In reasonably pure crystals of both these materials an increase in mobility can be obtained by cooling, but the maximum gain in silicon is only a factor of about two. In germanium a considerable change occurs, particularly for holes, the mobility increasing from 1,800 to about 15,000 cm$^2$/V sec as the temperature falls from 300 to 77° K. Mobilities vary over a wide range

15

for different samples of the same material, especially at low temperatures where the effects of impurities are strongest.

At field strengths exceeding about $10^3$ V/cm, $v_d$ is no longer strictly proportional to $F$, and $\mu$ ceases to be a constant. This is due to the effects of lattice scattering; $\mu$ decreases slowly as $F$ is increased, and for fields of the order $10^5$ V/cm, $v_d$ approaches a constant value.

## 1.8   CONDUCTIVITY OF SEMICONDUCTORS

The current carried across a unit cube of a solid is clearly the product of the electronic charge and the number of carriers entering or leaving opposite faces of the cube in unit time, i.e.,

$$i = q.n.v_n + q.p.v_p$$

where $v_n$ and $v_p$ are, respectively, the drift velocities of the electrons and holes, and $n$, $p$, are their concentrations. Dividing both sides of

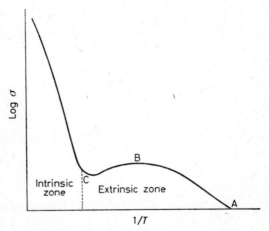

Figure 1.8. Temperature dependence of conductivity

this equation by the electric field, $E$ will give the conductivity. From eqn. (1.5), $\mu = v/F$, and therefore,

$$\sigma = q.n.\mu_n + q.p.\mu_p \qquad \dots (1.6)$$

Values of $n$ and $\mu$ both vary with temperature but at high temperatures the effect on carrier concentration is dominant, and the conductivity of a semiconductor then increases rapidly with temperature. This is one of the characteristics which distinguishes them from metals.

# CONDUCTIVITY OF SEMICONDUCTORS

The typical behaviour of a semiconductor is illustrated in *Figure 1.8*. The relationship has been plotted in the form $\log \sigma / T^{-1}$ in order to show the approximate exponential law which holds at low temperatures, between A and B, and at high temperatures where intrinsic conductivity is dominant [see eqn. (1.4)]. Since the extrinsic conduction depends on a smaller energy gap it becomes appreciable first as the temperature rises and is primarily responsible for the curve from A to C. Initially, at A, the curve shows increasing conductivity due to an increase in the carrier concentration as more impurity centres become ionized. The flattening at B indicates that the impurity centres are all ionized, so that no further increase can occur in the carrier concentration. The region from B to C is the zone of complete ionization referred to in Chapter 1.4, where the carrier concentration is constant and equal to the impurity concentration. The reduction in conductivity between B and C is due to reduced mobility (Chapter 1.7). The curve from C onwards is due to intrinsic conductivity, which rises very rapidly because of the high concentration of electrons in the valence band. Here, also, the change in conductivity is due to a change in the carrier concentration. The curve has a much greater slope than that near A because every electron near the top of the valence band is a probable source of a carrier pair, and these, of course, are far more numerous than the impurity centres.

Some experimental results for germanium are shown in *Figure 1.9*. From ambient temperatures upwards the intrinsic conductivity is dominant and the specimens doped with various impurities all give the same conductivity. Between 285 and 300° K three of the specimens show the breakaway into extrinsic conductivity; one sample of lightly doped $P$-type material, however, shows intrinsic conductivity down to 260° K.

Many semiconductor devices, including particle detectors, operate in the zone of complete ionization of the impurity centres (B to C of *Figure 1.8*), in which it is valid to assume that the carrier concentration is equal to the net impurity concentration. In this case, for an $N$-type crystal,

$$n = N_D$$

and $p$ is negligible.

The conductivity is, therefore

$$\sigma = q N_D \mu_n \qquad \qquad \ldots (1.7a)$$

Similarly, for a $P$-type crystal,

$$\sigma = q N_A \mu_p \qquad \qquad \ldots (1.7b)$$

17

The equations are very useful for approximate calculations. In the crystals used for detectors, $N_D$ or $N_A$ at ambient temperatures range from $10^{11}$ to $10^{14}$ per cm$^3$, and the corresponding conductivity from $10^{-5}$ to $10^{-2}$ $\Omega^{-1}$cm$^{-1}$.

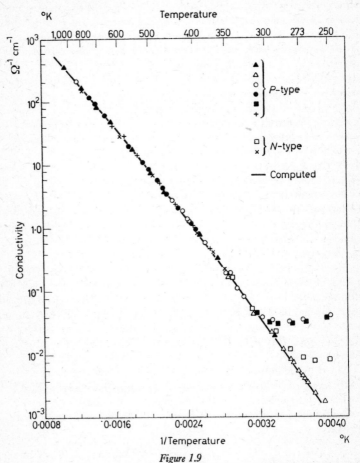

*Figure 1.9*

(F. J. Morin and J. P. Maita, *Phys. Rev.* 94 (1954) 1526, by courtesy of the American Physical Society)

## 1.9  TRAPPING AND CARRIER LIFETIME

It is necessary to focus attention again on the fact that the equilibrium condition of a semiconductor is maintained by a process of dynamic balance. Carriers are constantly being exchanged between their respective bands and the localized energy levels within the forbidden zone. The removal of a carrier from its condition of mobility to a localized level is termed 'trapping' and when this occurs the carrier is said to have been 'trapped'. At equilibrium, the trapping rate, for each type of carrier, is equal to what may be termed the 'release rate'. For this reason the use of the words 'trapping' and 'trap' is poor nomenclature, since it emphasizes one part of a process at the expense of its converse.

When considering the process of trapping it is customary to speak of any localized quantum state concerned as a 'trap', regardless of its other possible functions, e.g., as donor or acceptor. To be consistent and to simplify the problem, it is convenient, at least for the purpose of this section, to regard the process of recombination as one form of trapping; this is obviously logical since it has the same effect in removing carriers from their condition of mobility. On this basis, even a pure and perfect crystal would have a finite trapping rate. The presence of impurities or defects producing local energy levels in the forbidden zone increases the trapping rate, but not usually to the same extent for each carrier. This is true of all defect levels, whether they are donors or acceptors or lie deep in the energy gap.

The average time interval spent by a carrier in a condition of un-interrupted mobility is termed the 'mean lifetime' for that type of carrier, often abbreviated to 'lifetime'. This quantity obviously depends very much on the concentration of traps, and therefore on the parent crystal, its purity and perfection. It is often difficult to draw a clear distinction between the function of a defect centre as a donor or acceptor and its function as a trap. To help in this it is convenient to adopt another definition of trapping, describing it as 'a process which governs the mean lifetime of the carrier electrons or holes, or both'. The fact that the same process may also affect the carrier concentrations is not relevant. It is possible, for example, to have two samples of a given semiconductor with the same conductivity and the same carrier concentrations, but having vastly different concentrations of traps and very different carrier lifetimes. A sample of $P$-type silicon of 3,000 $\Omega$cm resistivity, for instance, could be obtained solely by refining until the residual impurity (usually boron) had been reduced to a concentration of $5 \cdot 0 \times 10^{12}$ atoms/cm$^3$. Another sample having the same resistivity could be obtained from less pure silicon by partial compensation with phosphorus; it could have $5 \cdot 0 \times 10^{13}$ atoms of boron and $4 \cdot 5 \times 10^{13}$ atoms of phosphorus/cm$^3$. The second sample would have a very much higher concentration of traps and a higher trapping rate. It would, therefore, have very much lower carrier lifetimes but its properties under equilibrium conditions at ambient temperatures would be very similar.

*Figure 1.10* illustrates the trapping processes in a hypothetical semiconductor having donor centres at a level $E_d$ and deeper centres at the level $E_T$. In a qualitative description of trapping it makes no difference whether the centres at $E_T$ have added electrons to the system (are of donor type) or have only created vacancies (are of acceptor type). Five processes are shown, the arrows indicating the electron transitions involved. A possible sixth process is the transition between $E_d$ and $E_T$, and its converse, but this has been omitted because it can only occur in the relatively improbable case of two centres being in close physical proximity. Processes 1, 2 and 4 begin

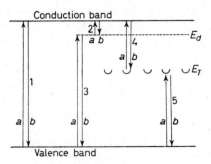

*Figure 1.10. Trapping processes*

and terminate the lifetimes of carrier electrons, while 1, 3 and 5 govern the lifetimes of the carrier holes. Processes 2*b* and 4*b* are electron trapping, 3*b* and 5*b* are hole trapping. Process 1 is 'direct recombination' and 'direct generation' of carrier pairs, and is a relatively rare occurrence. In an absolutely pure and perfect crystal this would be the only process operating, the crystal would be intrinsic and the carrier lifetime would be of the order of 1 sec in silicon. The very best silicon obtainable has a carrier lifetime at least two orders of magnitude below this.

Processes 2 and 3, taken together, are equivalent to process 1, and the same applies to processes 4 and 5. In practical cases generation and recombination occur almost exclusively in this way, through the agency of traps. Centres performing this function are commonly described as 'recombination centres' or 'recombination traps', a terminology which is also open to criticism because it emphasizes one function of the centre at the expense of its converse. These expressions, however, are now well established. According to the principle of detailed balancing each reverse process occurs with the same frequency as the forward process under equilibrium conditions[4].

If direct generation and recombination is included as a process of trapping the 'release rate' for electrons (paragraph 1 of this section) is also the generation rate and is balanced, at equilibrium, by the trapping rate. In Appendix B it is shown that the generation rate, $g$, (carriers/cm$^3$/sec) and the carrier lifetime, $\tau$, are linked by the relationships,

$$g_n = n/\tau_n \quad \text{for electrons} \qquad \ldots (1.8a)$$

and

$$g_p = p/\tau_p \quad \text{for holes} \qquad \ldots (1.8b)$$

Carrier concentrations and lifetimes can be measured, with difficulty, and such measurements are generally the only experimental evidence available on generation and trapping rates. The minority carrier lifetime is an important property of a crystal intended for use in making a detector. When quoting this figure it is common practice to refer to it simply as the 'carrier lifetime', it being understood that it refers to the minority carrier. In crystals of silicon or germanium selected for a detector the carrier lifetime is usually of the order $10^{-3}$ or $10^{-4}$ sec but is often reduced by an order of magnitude or more in processing. In other semiconductors the carrier lifetimes cannot, at present, be raised above about $10^{-6}$ sec, a figure which is too low for really satisfactory performance. The relationship between lifetimes and reaction rates, and the distribution of individual carrier lifetimes, is discussed in Appendix B. It appears that insulators, in general, owe their properties not only to a large energy gap, but also to very heavy trapping.

Another property of carriers, related to the lifetime, is 'diffusion length' ($L_n$ or $L_p$) which may be defined by the equation

$$L = \sqrt{(D\tau)} \qquad \ldots (1.9)$$

where $\tau$ is the lifetime and $D$ the diffusion coefficient. From a fundamental relationship, due to Einstein,

$$\mu = \frac{q}{kT} D \qquad \ldots (1.10)$$

It follows that

$$L^2 = \frac{kT\mu}{q} \tau \qquad \ldots (1.11)$$

Diffusion lengths in good silicon or germanium can be of the order of 1 mm.

Referring again to *Figure 1.10*, the electrons trapped in process 2$b$ do not all undergo process 3$b$. On the contrary, the vast majority,

21

under normal temperature conditions, are returned almost immediately to the conduction band. This assumes a typical operating temperature at which, under equilibrium conditions, the ionization of the donor centres is virtually complete. This type of trapping influences the apparent mobility of the carriers. At a lower temperature the effect becomes significant and is responsible for the 'impurity scattering' mentioned in 1.7.

## 1.10 TRANSIENT EFFECTS AND RELAXATION TIME

The effects of trapping are most clearly apparent in relation to transient effects and these are of prime importance in particle detection. It will be seen later that the concentration of carriers in a semiconductor may suddenly be increased by any of several possible events, but the absorption of a charged particle is the one of most importance in this study. Trapping is the main factor governing the speed with which the excess carriers are reabsorbed by the system.

It is desirable at this stage to distinguish between three types of trapping. The first may be termed 'generation, recombination trapping' and has already been described. It involves processes 1, or 2 and 3 together, or 5 and 4 together (*Figure 1.10*). The second involves processes 2 or 4 for electrons and 3 or 5 for holes, and was described in the last paragraph. For the purpose of this study it is termed 'scatter trapping', from its association with impurity scattering and its effect on mobility. The third type of trapping will be described in the next section. In most cases connected with particle detectors only the first two types of trapping need to be considered. When a transient occurs the dominant factor governing the speed with which the system returns to its equilibrium condition is generation, recombination trapping.

It is shown in Appendix B that if $n_1$ is the equilibrium concentration of one type of carrier and if a transient effect results in a small increase to $n_0$ at time $t = 0$, then the concentration falls to its equilibrium value exponentially,

$$n = n_1 + (n_0 - n_1) \exp{(-t/\tau)}$$

The relaxation time is the period taken for the excess concentration to fall to $1/e$ times its initial value and in this case is equal to the carrier lifetime $(\tau)$. This would not, in fact, apply to a very large transient since the carrier lifetime would not then remain constant, and the expression above is not of much value for calculations relevant to particle detection. It serves to show, however, that there is a link between carrier lifetime and relaxation time and that they are of the same order of magnitude.

## 1.11 SPACE CHARGE EFFECTS AND PHOTOCONDUCTIVITY

The third type of trapping arises when carriers are held for an appreciable period at a trapping centre. This happens not infrequently and arises from the particular characteristics of the local electron state involved[6]. Reference is made again to *Figure 1.10* and it is assumed that process 4 is much less probable than process 5. It is further assumed that the material is $N$-type, so that $E_T$ lies below the Fermi level and these traps normally contain electrons. If a transient effect now occurs which releases excess carriers of both kinds, a proportion of the excess holes in the valence band will be trapped at $E_T$ by process 5$b$. These holes will remain trapped after the system has otherwise returned to equilibrium through the operation of processes 2 and 3. Moreover, an approximately equal number of excess electrons will remain in the conduction band, simply because of the shortage of holes with which they can recombine. This is termed (by the author) 'space charge trapping', because it gives rise to a fixed space charge in the volume of the crystal which cannot be removed by the influence of an applied field.

It is fortunate that space charge trapping can be reduced to very small proportions in some semiconductors, certainly in silicon and germanium. When it occurs the crystal takes a relatively long time to return fully to its equilibrium condition, i.e., there is a long 'relaxation time'.

The significance of the term 'relaxation time' differs according to the process concerned. In connexion with space charge trapping a long relaxation time is detrimental to the operation of nearly all particle detectors, since it delays recovery of the crystal, and under rapid counting the effect will pile up. However, when referring to recombination trapping a long relaxation time is beneficial and, indeed, essential.

It was explained above that, in the presence of space charge trapping, a transient disturbance not only leaves a fixed space charge in the crystal for some little time but also leads to the retention for a similar period of an equal number of excess carriers of opposite sign. In fact, for a period defined by the relaxation time, the conductivity of the crystal is increased. Consider first the case of a crystal in isolation. The initial transient effect is assumed to create a considerable excess of both types of carrier. The return to equilibrium can only be effected by recombination, and if this process is arrested by the trapping of carriers of one type it cannot proceed to completion. Even if the crystal is in electrical contact with earth it will, nevertheless, retain the excess electrons because they are needed to conserve electrical neutrality. Looking at this point in another way, if the electron levels at $E_T$ in *Figure 1.10* become empty, then, (since the material is $N$-type and has a negligible hole concentration) they have, in effect, given up their electrons to the conduction band. Therefore, through the agency of the transient disturbance, they have become donors.

If the crystal is connected to electrodes and an electrical field applied, the excess electrons operate as carriers in just the same way as other electrons in the conduction band; they are swept out of the crystal by the field but are replaced by a stream of electrons 'injected' by the cathode. This temporary increase in conductivity is important in connexion with semiconductor counters but was first observed and, in fact, utilized in connexion with the photoconductivity of certain semiconductors.

A photon of sufficient energy, absorbed in a solid, can lift electrons into the conduction band. This may happen once or twice by Compton recoil, until the final transition, when the photon is absorbed. Semiconductors, having small energy gaps, respond readily to photons of relatively long wavelength. For example, radiation in the infra-red zone, near the visible spectrum, has a quantum energy in the region of $1 \cdot 3$ eV. This is more than twice the energy gap in germanium and the cut-off frequency for photo-response in a pure sample of this material is well below that of the visible spectrum.

Illumination is, therefore, one physical effect capable of producing a transient disturbance of the equilibrium condition in a semiconductor and thereby modifying its electrical properties. In the absence of space charge effects the increase in carrier concentration endures for only a very short period after the illumination ceases; a period of the same order as the carrier lifetime. Fast-acting photo cells (more correctly, 'photo diodes') are made from material of relatively short carrier lifetime and their speed of response when illumination is cut off is of the order of a microsecond or less.

Space charge trapping can be utilized in photo-sensitive devices to provide a simple means of amplification at the expense of time resolution. If a crystal is subjected to an electric field it will conduct current even in darkness, but the current will rise appreciably when the crystal is illuminated. If the illumination is a pulse of short duration and high intensity, the deliberate use of a crystal having space charge traps will preserve the effect for some period after the pulse, and the total excess charge passed can be larger by a factor of $10^4$ than it would be in the absence of space charge effects. The use of cadmium sulphide for this purpose is described by Dunlap[6]. Its use as a gamma fluxmeter and the possibilities for charged particles are described in Chapter 2.11. In the devices which exhibit this effect the immediate current, due to photo-carriers, is termed the 'primary current' and the later flow, due to space charge, is the 'secondary current'.

## 1.12  SURFACE EFFECTS

The surfaces of semiconductor crystals invariably have electrical properties differing from those of the bulk material. These properties are usually very variable, being strongly dependent on the physical form of the surface, on surface contamination and on the ambient atmosphere. The theory of surface effects is a very extensive study, most of which is outside the scope of this work, but a qualitative understanding of some points is necessary for a critical appreciation of detector design.

At the surface there are additional localized energy levels which arise from the non-uniform distribution of atomic cores. There are usually further localized energy levels arising from oxidation and contamination. The surface layer therefore contains a space charge, which alters the whole energy band system and moves the energy gap relative to its position in the bulk material. It often happens that an 'inversion layer' is created, in which the conductivity is of the opposite type from that in the bulk. With or without an inversion layer it is usual for the conductivity to be greater on the surface than in the bulk; this effect is often very marked where surface contamination is appreciable, and a moist atmosphere is a common cause of high surface conductivity.

The higher concentration of local energy levels at the surface leads to increased trapping, especially recombination trapping. In many semiconductor specimens having dimensions of only a few millimetres the surface trapping rate is relatively so high that the majority of the carriers begin and end their lives at the surface. The carrier lifetime is, therefore, a function of crystal size and shape, and it is customary to refer to 'bulk lifetime', where a figure has been corrected for surface effects. Surface trapping can be kept to a minimum only by very careful control of contamination and the condition of the surface.

Surface conductivity is an adverse factor in all types of semiconductor detector, because it gives rise to 'surface leakage current' by-passing the sensitive volume. This is one cause of electrical noise, which limits energy resolution. Surface trapping (or surface recombination and generation, to be more precise) is detrimental because it reduces the effective lifetime of the carriers and gives rise to collection problems. However, this also contributes to electrical noise which is often more serious.

## 1.13   RADIATION INDUCED CONDUCTIVITY AND CRYSTAL COUNTERS

The absorption of charged particles in some solids has effects similar to those of photoconductivity. A single particle, however, will release a very large number of electrons and holes, and the result is similar to that of ionization in a gaseous counter.

Under normal conditions, and provided that no nuclear reaction occurs, the number of excess carriers released is closely proportional to the energy of the incident particle, being almost completely independent of the nature of the particle and of environmental factors

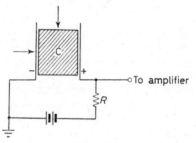

*Figure 1.11*

such as temperature, pressure and (within wide limits) electric field. The energy absorbed per carrier pair is a constant of the basic crystal and is less by a factor up to about 10 than the energy per ion pair in gaseous ionization ($\sim 30\,\text{eV}$). This gives a substantially greater charge release without resort to multiplication (which, in any case, can only occur in solids in most exceptional circumstances). Even highly energetic particles can be stopped and the whole of their energy released within a relatively small volume, the stopping power of a solid being roughly $10^3$ times that of a gas at s.t.p. These characteristics of carrier production by charged particles in solids are obviously desirable features in relation to the possibility of using the process for particle detectors.

The action of a crystal counter is illustrated in principle in *Figure 1.11*. A block of crystal having dimensions about 1 cm or less is coated on opposite faces with conducting material to provide electrodes. The resistance of the crystal and that of the load, $R$, must both be very high and a substantial electric field is applied across the crystal. The electrode connected to the resistor is the 'collector', not necessarily positive. A charged particle may enter through one of the electrodes or through another face of the crystal; in either event it is absorbed with the creation of a number of electron-hole pairs. These carriers are swept out of the crystal by the electric field and the resulting pulse of potential at the collector can be amplified to operate a counter.

Unfortunately, as is now a matter of history, experiments of this kind with various crystalline materials have not been very successful, due mainly to problems arising from trapping. In order to achieve good linearity it is necessary to obtain either complete collection of the carriers or to collect a constant proportion of them despite variations in particle nature, energy, point of entry and counting rate. The only very satisfactory solution is to aim for complete collection. The description of solid state conduction given in previous sections enables the characteristics required of a detector crystal to be stated as follows:

(1) *High resistivity*—The electric field must be high enough to give complete carrier collection in a short interval of time, in order to minimize carrier losses by trapping and to give fast pulses. High resistivity is therefore needed to enable an adequate electric field to be applied without passing much current.

(2) *High carrier mobility*—This, too, is needed to give rapid carrier collection, and for the same reasons.

(3) *Low trapping rate*—Recombination trapping reduces the efficiency of collection. Space charge trapping does this but also leads to increased crystal conductivity and modifies the electric field; both factors cause a change in response as irradiation proceeds. Scatter trapping reduces mobility.

(4) *Low energy gap*—The number of carrier pairs released for a given particle energy will be larger for low values of $E_G$.

(5) *High stability*—The above properties must be retained and remain constant under prolonged subjection to the electric field and repeated irradiation.

It may be noted here that (1) is inconsistent with (2) and (4).

In order to obtain a sufficiently high electric field for efficient collection without passing excessive current, much of the work on crystal detectors has been concentrated on diamond,[7] cadmium sulphide[8] and zinc sulphide,[9] which could properly be regarded as insulators but show irradiation conductivity. Van Heerden[10] used silver chloride, a semiconductor, and found it necessary to cool with liquid air or nitrogen to cut down the conductivity. The results of this work have not been encouraging, the main problem being the high density of trapping centres. Using these materials, a substantial proportion of the carriers created by an incident particle are caught by traps before they can be collected, and there is a considerable amount of space charge trapping. The results are described in the following paragraph[11]:

'If a crystal counter has been exposed to radiation and an electric field for a prolonged period, the separated positive and negative charges will build up a space charge which modifies the field to such an extent that the pulses will become smaller. Moreover, the positive holes will act as trapping centres for electrons passing in their vicinity (and, of course, vice versa). It is, therefore, necessary to remove the space charges periodically, for instance, by annealing or field reversal'[11, p. 49].

Champion[12] and Stratton[13] have had some success with carefully selected diamonds. They report a trial using beta radiation in which, with applied fields in excess of 8,000 V/cm stability was obtained. Linearity with energy, however, was only approximate. Their results are summarized below:

(a) Only a proportion of diamonds exhibit counting properties at all and relatively few are good (25 in 200).

(b) For a given type of particle there is at least a qualitative relationship between energy and pulse height, and between energy and counting efficiency.

(c) α-particles of 5 MeV gave, at best, pulses only three times the height of those from 1 MeV β-particles. This is due to surface layers having a higher concentration of traps.

(d) Diamonds can show a big variation in counting properties (by a factor of 10) in different parts of the same crystal.

Despite the shortcomings of crystal counters they have found applications in experimental work. Scintillation counters, however, have hitherto largely filled the need for solid state detectors and are much superior to crystal counters for most applications, despite their need for photomultipliers and the attendant electronic problems. The ensuing sections of this work describe how the properties of some semiconductors can be utilized to overcome both the trapping problem and that of obtaining a high electric field with only moderate current flow.

## 1.14  COLLECTING TIME AND CARRIER LIFETIME

The dominant factor governing the use of crystal counters is the trapping problem. It appears not unreasonable to argue that 99 per cent of the carriers should be collected, not only for the sake of maintaining good energy resolution but, even more important, to avoid leaving space charge in the crystal. Let $t_c$ be the collecting time for a device such as that of *Figure 1.11*: i.e. the time required to sweep the slowest of the excess carriers out of the crystal. Carrier lifetimes have an exponential distribution (see Appendix B) and

$$f = e^{-t/\tau}$$

where $f$ is the fraction of the excess carriers left after a time, $t$. Putting $f = 0.99$ gives a time limit for collection,

$$t_c \gg 10^{-2}\tau \qquad \ldots (1.12)$$

This condition can be met, at least in some types of semiconductor detector. In others the condition is, apparently, not met but reasonably good results are nevertheless obtained, in fact, it appears that a more practical limit would be

$$t_c \gg 10^{-1}\tau \qquad \ldots (1.13)$$

There are several possible explanations for the performance being, in this respect, better than theory and these are stated below:

   (a) In the semiconductor counters concerned there is often little or no space charge trapping, so that incomplete collection would only affect energy resolution.

   (b) The effect of losing a carrier is not proportional to the charge it carries. The signal obtained depends on the work done on the carriers during collection and a lost carrier contributes in proportion to the distance travelled before it was trapped.

   (c) There is often some doubt about the actual mean lifetime of the excess carriers being collected. The estimated lifetime (and it is usually not much better than an estimate) of the minority carrier at equilibrium is the usual starting point for calculations on the problem, and this may well be pessimistic in relation to the lifetimes of the excess carriers produced by a transient. This can happen, for example, if the 'effective minority carrier lifetime' used includes strong surface effects.

### REFERENCES

[1] KITTEL, C., *Introduction to Solid State Physics*, Wiley, New York (1953)
[2] CUSACK, N., *Electrical and Magnetic Properties of Solids*, Longmans, London (1958)
[3] COLLINS, C. B. *et al.*, *Phys. Rev.* 105 (1957) 1168
[4] BRIDGEMAN, P. W. *Phys. Rev.* 31 (1928) 101

[5] EHRENBERG, W., *Electric Conduction in Semiconductors and Metals*, Clarendon, Oxford (1958)

[6] DUNLAP, W. C., *An Introduction to Semiconductors*, Wiley, New York (1957)

[7] WOOLDRIDGE, D. E., AHEARN, A. J., and BURTON, J. A., *Phys. Rev.* 71 (1947) 913

[8] FRERICHS, P. R., *Phys. Rev.* 72 (1947) 594

[9] AHEARN, A. J., *Phys. Rev.* 73 (1948) 524

[10] VAN HEERDEN, P. J., *The Crystal Counter, a New Instrument in Nuclear Physics*, Noord Hollandische Uitgevers Maatschappij, Amsterdam (1945)

[11] SEGRÉ, E. (Ed.), *Experimental Nuclear Physics*, Vol. 1, Wiley, New York (1953)

[12] CHAMPION, F. C., *Proc. phys. Soc. Lond.*, B65, 7, 465

[13] STRATTON, K. and CHAMPION, F. C., *Proc. phys. Soc. Lond.*, B65, 7, 473

# 2

# BULK SEMICONDUCTOR DETECTORS

## 2.1 INTRODUCTION

AT THIS stage it is convenient to describe one class of semiconductor detector, 'bulk' detectors. Some writers refer to them as 'bulk conductivity counters', or simply 'conductivity counters', but this is rather a misnomer because their success depends not on conductivity but on very high resistivity. This type is, in its operating principles, the simplest class but in the present state of development there is, unfortunately, very little information on its performance. The other types of semiconductor detector, to be described later, suffer from the disability that they can only be made with rather limited sensitive volumes. Bulk detectors are better in this respect although it is still difficult to obtain good performance from a detector larger than about 1 cm³. Primarily because of their larger sensitive volumes, bulk counters do not give the performance figures quoted in the introduction to this study. They do, however, have a greater range of linearity for charged particles and greater sensitivity to $\beta$- and $\gamma$-radiation. There is a requirement for a simple, high efficiency linear detector for $\gamma$-radiation, to replace the scintillation counter in many applications. Bulk detectors may meet this need with a little more development.

A bulk detector is a new form of crystal detector and, superficially, differs from its predecessors only in the use of a single-crystal block of semiconductor in place of the more usual insulating crystal. Development is primarily a problem of finding better materials. Although semiconductor crystals can be obtained which meet the carrier lifetime requirement, they still do not readily solve the problem because their conductivity at ambient temperatures is too high. They therefore tend to pass excessive current when not under radiation ('dark' current) and this causes a high noise level. Excessive current can also lead to heating of the crystal and consequent loss of stability. For really satisfactory results the resistivity should approach that of an insulator; true intrinsic silicon, if it could be obtained, would not be sufficiently resistive at ambient temperatures and germanium is unsatisfactory even when cooled by liquid nitrogen.

31

Three different approaches have so far been reported and will be described in some detail later. All three, however, require the solution of a different problem before any very satisfactory results can be achieved; this difficulty and its remedy are discussed in the next section.

## 2.2 Ohmic Contacts

When an ordinary electrical contact is made between a metal and a semiconductor the junction forms a narrow rectifying barrier. This phenomenon is described in greater detail in Chapter 3, where the physical causes and consequences are very relevant to another type of detector. For the present purpose it is only necessary to point out that such a barrier would ordinarily exist at one or other of the electrodes in a bulk detector and steps must be taken to prevent it, otherwise nearly all the applied potential would appear across the barrier and only a small electric field would be applied to the bulk of the crystal.

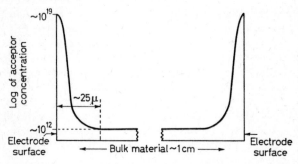

Figure 2.1. General form of the impurity concentration in a P-type silicon bulk detector

An electrical contact of special form, which does not have a rectifying barrier, is termed an 'ohmic contact' and depends for its success on avoiding any sharp change of conductivity. A smooth relationship between conductivity and depth from the electrode surface is obtained by graded doping with impurity, as illustrated in Figure 2.1. There are several methods of surface doping in this way, but gaseous diffusion is the one usually employed and is probably the best. Some details of the method are described in Chapter 2.6. For a really good ohmic contact the change in Fermi level should not exceed 1 $kT$ over a distance equal to the diffusion length of the carriers. The heavily doped regions close to the electrodes have, of course, low carrier

32

lifetimes and therefore short diffusion lengths. Another type of ohmic contact is described in Chapter 10.2.

## 2.3 Properties of the Bulk Material

To overcome the problem of dark current the resistivity of the bulk of the crystal should be at least $10^7 \, \Omega\,cm$, which is two orders of magnitude greater than that of intrinsic silicon at ambient temperatures. The obvious method of obtaining such low resistivity is to use the detector at a very low temperature and an ordinary crystal of highly refined silicon would have resistivity of this order at about $20°\,K$. There are several problems in operating at a temperature as low as this, one of which is a tendency for carrier multiplication to occur with consequent erratic behaviour.

The necessary high resistivity can be obtained at a more practical temperature, in the region of $100°\,K$, if the silicon is intrinsic or nearly so. Other semiconductors, having a larger energy gap, can meet the resistivity requirement even at ambient temperature but these tend to have short carrier lifetimes with present techniques of manufacture. Gallium arsenide ($E_G = 1\cdot39$) appears to be a hopeful material and is under investigation. Whichever material is to be used it is necessary that it first be rendered effectively intrinsic and it has already been explained that this presents difficulties. The methods employed at present all depend on compensation by impurity centres lying deep in the forbidden zone. They are described in more detail in Chapters 2.5 and 2.6.

## 2.4 Principles of Operation

Bulk detectors are probably best operated with the aperture on one of the free faces of the crystal, thereby avoiding any 'window' effect, due to absorption of the particle energy by the electrodes. *Figure 2.2* illustrates the entry of two particles of different energy. Although shown, for convenience, on the same diagram it must be appreciated that they represent successive events. The shaded areas indicate, diagrammatically, the intensity of carrier formation along the particle tracks; they do not, of course, ever have a distribution in space of this form.

The voltage pulse develops across the load resistor, $R_L$ as the carriers are collected by the electrodes. The height of the pulse, for a given charge collected, is governed primarily by the parallel capacitance in the circuit, $C_d$ being that of the crystal and $C_a$ the stray capacitances plus that of the amplifier input. Development of full pulse height, and also the rate of pulse decay, is governed by the time constant, $RC$. In the simple circuit of *Figure 2.2*,

$$\frac{1}{R} = \frac{1}{R_L} + \frac{1}{R_d} \quad \text{and} \quad C = C_a + C_d$$

Because the carriers have different mobilities the charge-collecting time will differ according to the position of the particle track. Since the hole mobility is the limiting factor, collection will take longer for particle A than for B.

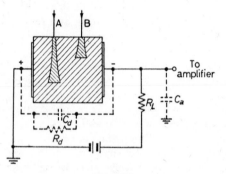

*Figure 2.2*

This is an old problem in gaseous ion counters, where the ion mobilities differ sufficiently that the effect of the positive ions can be eliminated by suitable clipping, and operation obtained on the negative ions alone. The use of a grid or cylindrical geometry then gives nearly constant collecting time. In this case no such remedies are available and if good proportionality of pulse height with particle energy is to be achieved the only obvious method is to use a relatively long decay constant and obtain virtually complete collection for all particle tracks. It is usual to set the input decay constant ($RC$, above) even longer than is necessary for this and to set the decay constant of the amplifier at a suitable value for pulse clipping. For bulk detectors, which have relatively long pulse rise times, there may be some advantage in using delay line clipping but this has not been reported. Clipping times are kept as short as possible, subject to the need for complete collection, in order to reduce the effects of noise.

In the case of semiconductor detectors (and crystal detectors generally) there is normally no carrier multiplication. This has the disadvantage that the voltage pulses obtained at the electrodes are

34

only of the order of a few millivolts and amplification by a factor of about 1,000 is needed for display, or to operate a counter. On the other hand, the absence of multiplication reduces the statistical variation in the charge released and the theoretical limit of resolution is higher.

If the mobility is known, the collecting time for any particular applied field can readily be estimated. For example, in a good silicon crystal at 90° K the hole mobility is the limiting factor on collecting time and is in the region of 1,000 cm$^2$/V sec. If the detector is a 6-mm cube with a field of 1,000 V/cm the maximum collecting time (transit time) is

$$\frac{0{\cdot}6}{10^3 \times 10^3} = 0{\cdot}6 \ \mu\text{sec}$$

Miller et al.[1] have pointed out that the actual collecting time will exceed the value calculated in this way from the mobility and the applied field because allowance should be made for the initial period when the carriers move slowly, while still under the influence of their mutual attraction (ambipolar effect). They demonstrated this effect using fission fragments but its magnitude is not important in relation to a rough calculation of this kind.

The energy loss per carrier pair in silicon is about 3·6 eV, so that a particle of energy 30 MeV would release $8 \times 10^6$ ion pairs and the charge collected would be $1{\cdot}3 \times 10^{-12}$ C. The detector capacitance is negligible, but the amplifier input may have a capacitance of about 50–100 pF. On this basis the voltage pulse could be of the order 10 mV.

In common with other semiconductor detectors, bulk counters are photo sensitive and must therefore be used in darkness. Surface cleanliness and condition are important factors in reducing the surface leakage current and use in a dry atmosphere is essential. Operation in a vacuum is better still (Jackson et al.[2]).

## 2.5   THE GOLD SILICON BULK DETECTOR

As stated earlier, three approaches have so far been reported to the problem of obtaining sufficiently high resistivity. This approach was described by Davis[3] and also by Van Putten and Vander Velde[4] who used their detector to investigate the energy loss distribution of negative pions at 1·5 GeV/c and 2·55 GeV/c. The starting material is $N$-type silicon doped uniformly with gold. The gold produces energy levels deep in the forbidden zone and brings down the Fermi level, as described in Chapter 1.4.

It is found that if the concentration of gold atoms is about three times that of the donor centres, the Fermi level lies close to the middle of the gap over a wide range of temperature, and the material is approximately intrinsic. However, the relatively heavy doping involved has the drawback that it increases trapping and seriously reduces the carrier lifetime. In the crystal described by Van Putten and Vander Velde[4], the concentration of donor atoms (phosphorus) was about $2 \times 10^{14}$ and that of gold about $5 \times 10^{14}$. At $120° K$ the resistivity exceeded $10^9 \ \Omega cm$. It is stated that under a field of 2,000 V/cm the mean drift path was about 1 cm and the crystal thickness was 0·25 cm. On this basis the lifetime was only about four times as great as the collecting time and there must have been an appreciable loss of carriers. This would not have any noticeable effect on resolution in an experiment with very high energy mesons, because resolution would in any event be poor, due to Landau effect. Van Putten and Vander Velde did not observe any space charge effects, and it may therefore be concluded that there was little space charge trapping in their crystal. On the other hand, space charge effect would not be readily apparent under these conditions if the contacts were not good ohmic contacts.

The counter used by Davies[3] had a greater total impurity concentration, of the order $10^{16}/cm^3$, and the hole lifetime was stated to be only $10^{-9}$ sec. When fitted with ohmic contacts this counter gave very strong space charge effects which were investigated by bombarding, through the negative electrode, with 5 MeV $\alpha$-particles. The results were erratic, but some pulses gave very considerable secondary currents with decay time constants of $10-100$ $\mu$sec. Davies also refers to a counter in $P$-type silicon which had better carrier lifetimes ($10^{-7}$ sec for holes).

The ohmic contacts to this type of detector can best be made by further doping (by diffusion) with gold. A good method[3] is to deposit the gold by vaporization *in vacuo* at $400-500°$ C. Connexions can be made with gold wire fused on at the same temperature. There is no need to apply any additional metal coating, since the surface conductivity obtained in this way is fully adequate to form the electrodes.

## 2.6 THE BORON SILICON BULK DETECTOR

This detector depends on a similar compensation effect to that obtained in the gold silicon crystal, but the method of preparation differs and improved carrier lifetime is obtained. It is described by D. C. Northrop (private communication) and depends on a heat treatment of $P$-type silicon, containing boron as residual impurity. At

1,000–1,100° C an internal modification of the crystal structure occurs which again brings the Fermi level close to the middle of the energy gap and renders the material approximately intrinsic. The process is not well understood but it is suggested by Northrop that it is due to an impurity defect (probably caused by oxygen) which changes its form on heating and then produces deep hole traps. Careful control of time and temperature is needed to obtain the desired resistivity and, even more so, to control the effect on carrier lifetime.

As an example of a method of making a bulk detector the process of preparation employed for a number of successful crystals is described below. It is emphasized that this is purely an example and that techniques are constantly improving.

### Boron Silicon Bulk Detector: Method of Preparation

The starting material is $P$-type silicon of resistivity 5,000–6,000 $\Omega$ cm and minority carrier lifetime about 1 msec. This is cut to make a 6 mm cube, ground and polished on all surfaces.

All faces are etched in 80:20† nitric acid and hydrofluoric acid at 40–50° C. The etch is quenched with demineralized water at intervals of one minute and the crystal is washed and examined microscopically. After about 5 min of treatment the crystal is found to have smooth unblemished surfaces and etching is discontinued. During this and subsequent processes the crystal is not touched by hand.

The crystal is then subjected to boron diffusion at 1,100° C. This is carried out in a heated tube carrying a flow of dry nitrogen and a boat filled with boric anhydride is contained in the tube, upstream from the crystal. The process takes about 4 h and serves the dual purpose of providing a borated surface for ohmic contacts and giving the necessary heat treatment. At this stage the resistivity of the bulk material rises to about 60,000 $\Omega$ cm at ambient temperature and the carrier lifetime is reduced to about 30 $\mu$ sec. These effects, however, vary over a very wide range from crystal to crystal.

The diffusion leaves all the surfaces coated with boron glass, which is removed by soaking in concentrated hydrofluoric acid and washing. The two electrode faces are then masked with wax and the remaining four faces are etched again at 40–50° C for about half an hour. This removes the diffused layer and completion of the process is checked by

---

† As an alternative, C.P. 4 may be used with no apparent difference in results. The composition is:

| | | | | |
|---|---|---|---|---|
| nitric acid | . | . | . | 25 vol. |
| hydrofluoric acid | . | . | . | 15 vol. |
| anhydrous acetic acid | . | . | . | 15 vol. |
| bromine | . | . | . | 0·3 vol. |

37

measuring the surface resistivity with probes. The wax is removed with toluene in an ultrasonic bath and the crystal dried with alcohol.

The connexions to the electrode faces can now be made by simply fusing on to each a thin wire of gold containing about 1 per cent boron. The crystal is heated to 400° C, the wire is pressed on to the surface and the whole allowed to cool. A better alternative is to coat these surfaces with aluminium by vaporization *in vacuo* to a thickness of about 10$\mu$ and then heat to 600° C. Pressure contacts can then be used, or wires may be attached with silver paste.

It is possible to obtain an ohmic contact solely by alloying with aluminium, the boron diffusion then being unnecessary. The aluminium is applied by vacuum deposition, as described above, and the crystal is then heat treated at 600° C or more, according to the silicon condition desired. This method gives a detector of resistivity at ambient temperature in the region of $6 \times 10^4$ $\Omega$cm and at a suitable operating temperature it will be about $5 \times 10^8$ $\Omega$cm. At low temperature the carrier lifetime is further reduced but remains well above 1 $\mu$sec.

### The Phosphorus Silicon Bulk Detector

This is described by Griffith *et al.*[5] and was made by Gibbons and Northrop. The bulk material was $N$-type and very close to intrinsic, having a resistivity of $10^9$ $\Omega$cm at 90° K. It was made from $P$-type silicon by the same sort of heat treatment described above which, if carried far enough, will convert the material to $N$-type. The ohmic contacts were made by phosphorus diffusion.

## 2.7  THE GALLIUM ARSENIDE BULK DETECTOR

This is not, in its present state of development, a satisfactory counter, but is mentioned here because it represents the closest approach yet made to a bulk detector which operates at ambient temperatures. The material is selected for the purpose because it combines a large energy gap (1·39 eV) and therefore high intrinsic resistivity, with a carrier lifetime approaching the value required.

The technique of manufacture depends primarily on zone refining which, if carried out in an inert gas, can produce $N$-type material with about $10^{16}$ electrons/cm$^3$, originating from a shallow donor. If oxygen is present during preparation, a material of resistivity $10^8$–$10^9$ $\Omega$cm, still $N$-type, can be obtained. This is thought to be due to a process of compensation by deep traps similar to the two processes described above. Ohmic contacts are made by alloying with Indium;

a bead of metal is put on to the surface, melted and then alloyed at 400° C.

Further success in development of this type of detector depends mainly on improving the carrier lifetime; $10^{-8}$sec is about the best obtained so far.

## 2.8   OPERATING CONDITIONS AND LIMITATIONS

The dominant limitation is that of carrier lifetime and the problem is usually reduced to a minimum by applying the highest field possible, subject to the need for low dark current. The conductivity varies over a wide range, partly because of variations in the bulk material and partly because of differences in the surface condition. A substantial proportion of the dark current is due to surface leakage and surface effects therefore play a large part. However, the optimum field usually lies in the region of 1,000–2,000 V/cm and the dark current is a few microamps.

The width between electrodes is limited by carrier lifetime to one or two centimetres. The depth and breadth are limited to roughly the same figure by the dark current problem and by homogeneity considerations. A 1 cm cube of silicon would absorb protons of 50 MeV and $\alpha$-particles up to 200 MeV, approximately. For higher energies special geometry is advantageous; for example, high resistance may be preserved by reducing the depth in proportion to the increase in length and using a small aperture.

With boron silicon bulk detectors there is another problem, which arises from the method of manufacture. Whatever may be the true mechanism of compensation brought about by the heat treatment, it appears that it does not give uniform results, the crystals being non-homogeneous in trap concentration and carrier lifetime. The latter may vary by as much as two or three orders of magnitude according to the position of the carrier tracks. Even with the best counters, energy resolution seems to be limited by this factor rather than by electrical noise or the statistical variations in carrier production.

It has been mentioned earlier (1.14) that semiconductor counters give better charge collection than would be expected on the basis of a simple comparison between the transit time and the mean carrier lifetime. Some of the obvious explanations have also been mentioned. It is suggested (by the author) that, in the case of bulk counters, a further explanation may be found in the presence of space charge effects (see Chapter 1.11). In boron silicon bulk counters there is no obvious space charge trapping but, of course, there is no fundamental difference between this and the short term (scatter) trapping which is

39

known to occur. It is, therefore, to be expected that when carriers are lost by their retention, even for a short period, in traps, a charge may nevertheless reach the collector by virtue of the increased conductivity caused by a small space charge effect.

The choice of materials for bulk counters is at present dictated almost entirely by the problems of resistivity and lifetime. As these problems are overcome in materials other than silicon it will be profitable to bear in mind the advantages of using materials of high nuclear mass, thus reducing the penetration of high energy particles and extending the range of proportionality with a counter of a given size. For gamma detection this would also give much increased sensitivity from the greater photo-electric response.

## 2.9   Noise in Bulk Detectors

The subject of electrical noise in semiconductors and devices made from them is an extensive study which cannot be discussed adequately in this work. A fairly complete account of the subject is given by Van der Ziel[6] which is the source of most of the information here. An interesting new approach to the problem, which covers the practical aspects and includes the associated electronic equipment is reported by Fairstein[7].†

The noise emanating from a bulk detector can be classified under three headings:

*Thermal noise*—This is due to fluctuations in the spatial distribution of the carriers, arising from thermal diffusion, and has the same form as the noise associated with an electrical resistor, often termed 'Johnson noise'. Theoretically it is present even in the absence of an applied field and its magnitude does not depend on the voltage or the dark current. The equivalent current generated is given by

$$\overline{i^2} = 4kT.G.\Delta f \qquad \ldots (2.1)$$

where $G$ is the conductivity of the detector and $\Delta f$ is the bandwidth.

*Current noise*—This is often termed 'shot noise' from analogy with a similar source of noise in thermionic valves. It is due, in semiconductors, to statistical fluctuations in the number of carriers, leading to changes in conductivity, and the noise power is proportional to the current flowing. The mean square noise current is

$$\overline{i^2} = 2qI.\Delta f \qquad \ldots (2.2)$$

where $I$ is the dark current.

† The sources of noise in bulk counters are very well described in a recent publication[13].

*Flicker noise*—This is distinguished from thermal and current noise by the fact that it is frequency-dependent. The mean square current is

$$\overline{i^2} \propto \frac{1}{f^n}$$

where $n$ is approximately unity, and is almost independent of temperature. Because of the frequency dependence, this type of noise is often termed 'one over $f$' noise.

The causes of flicker noise are still not very well understood but it appears to originate in the surface of the material and the condition of the surface profoundly affects its magnitude. According to Fonger[8] there are two types of flicker noise in semiconductor devices, one is described as 'surface flicker noise' and appears to have its origin in recombination of the carriers in surface traps; the other is termed 'leakage current noise' and originates in the flow of current through the surface layer of the material. It is to be expected that both will be present in bulk detectors but the surface flicker noise power depends on the number of carriers available to interact with the surface states, and is therefore likely to be small in a device of such high resistance as a bulk detector. Leakage noise is, therefore, likely to be the dominant form of flicker noise.

Fonger's measurements show that the leakage noise is proportional to the square of the surface current, $I_L$, and therefore

$$\overline{i^2} \propto \frac{I_L^2}{f} \Delta f \qquad \qquad \ldots (2.3)$$

It is not possible at present to give even an empirical relation which will express this noise power solely in terms of the operating conditions.

Turning now to the question of reducing noise to a minimum, current noise and thermal noise are relatively simple problems and are amenable, in the sense that the low conductivity which is desirable for the reduction of current noise is also effective in reducing thermal noise. Operation at low temperatures, too, is beneficial on both counts. Flicker noise is more difficult but it is obvious that every effort to reduce the surface leakage current (e.g. by keeping the surface smooth, clean and dry) will be very rewarding, and this is found in practice to be the case. In general, thermal noise is negligible in semiconductor counters. Flicker noise varies over a range of several orders of magnitude but, in bulk counters, can usually be reduced to a level at which its effects are smaller than those of current noise.

Excessive flicker noise can arise from a faulty contact and the adhesion of the connexions is therefore important. It should also be noted that both thermal and flicker noise are geometry-sensitive. It is necessary to ensure that amplifier noise does not limit resolution; many amplifiers are likely to be more troublesome in this respect than the counter.

The description of the noise problem given above follows conventional methods for the definition of electrical noise and its dependence on current, conductivity and so on. For a qualitative discussion of the problem in relation to optimization of the detector design this is, perhaps, the best approach. For a detailed mathematical treatment, and for problems relating to the optimization of the system as a whole, it is suggested by Fairstein[7] that a better approach is to define noise in relation to the fluctuations of charge involved. This proposal arises from the fact that detectors are, from the electronics point of view, charge-collecting devices and Fairstein suggests the adoption of an equivalent noise charge, $Q_e$, or equilvaent electrons, $N_e$ ($Q_e$ in coulombs = $1 \cdot 6 \times 10^{-19} N_e$). The following definition is quoted: 'The equivalent noise charge, in r.m.s. coulombs, is that quantity of charge which, if applied to the input of the amplifier in a time short compared with the amplifier response time, would produce an output voltage pulse of amplitude just equal to the observed r.m.s. noise voltage.'

An even better rationalization of the noise problem in detectors is used by Hansen and Goulding[9], who express the noise power in $(\text{keV})^2$, thus relating it directly to energy resolution.

## 2.10   PERFORMANCE AND APPLICATIONS

Only a little information is available, as yet, on the performance of bulk counters with charged particles but a report from Dr. Northrop (private communication) mentions a resolution of 1 per cent with approximately 5 MeV $\alpha$-particles. A report by Griffith *et al.*[5] describes some work with a 6 mm cube $N$-type counter in which a resolution of 6·6 per cent (f.w.h.m) was obtained with 30-MeV protons, but it appears that this refers to a geometry in which the particles entered through one of the electrodes.

There is considerable interest in the possibility of using bulk counters for improved gamma detection. The low atomic number of silicon makes it very difficult to obtain a $\gamma$-spectrum which shows a photopeak, particularly if the gamma energy exceeds a few hundred keV, but individual photons giving a Compton electron are readily counted. A $\gamma$-spectrum from cobalt 60 is shown in *Figure 2.3*, in which the two Compton edges are clearly resolved. A spectrum of the monoenergetic (660 keV) emission of caesium 137 is shown in *Figure 2.4*. In both these results the resolution on the Compton edge is equivalent to about 6 per cent (f.w.h.m.). These spectra were obtained with 6 mm cubic boron silicon counters at 80° K, using pulse height analysis as described in Appendix D. The collecting field was 1,000 V/cm and the signal to noise ratio was 50 : 1 with a clipping time constant of 3·2 $\mu$sec. Comparison with the results obtained using lithium ion drift detectors, described in Chapter 7.5 suggests that a photopeak could have been obtained in these experiments by increasing the recording time, at least with caesium 137.

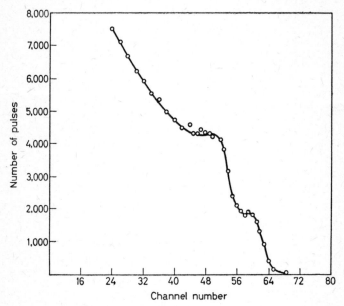

*Figure 2.3 γ-spectrum* $^{60}$Co *(1·33 1·17* MeV)

(D. C. Northrop and P. E. Gibbons, *Proc. Phys. Soc.* (July 1962), by courtesy of Institute of Physics)

With further development of bulk counters for use at ambient temperatures it seems probable that their stability, simplicity and small size will be of value in applications as gamma fluxmeters, particularly for health physics monitoring. Bulk counters are known to be sensitive to $\beta$-particles but no results have yet been published. Comparison with other types of semiconductor counter (see Chapter 7.5) suggests that they would be likely to give a similar response and over a greater energy range. For particle spectrometry they again have the advantage of covering a greater energy range but, at present, with inferior resolution both in energy and time.

Neutrons react with silicon in at least four ways[10], but the threshold energies are all in excess of 2·5 MeV. Counters in silicon are, therefore, insensitive to neutrons of low energy and could be used to detect other radiations in a flux of thermal neutrons. For neutrons of higher energy the reaction cross-sections are appreciable. Considering the possibilities of a neutron detector, these reactions complicate the problem

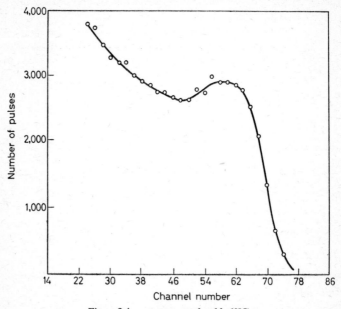

*Figure 2.4. γ-spectrum produced by* [137]Cs

(D. C. Northrop and P. E. Gibbons, *Proc. Phys. Soc.* (July 1962), by courtesy of Institute of Physics)

rather than assist it. It is possible to make a detector for neutrons by applying a coating of fissile material such as $^6$LiF to the aperture face, but this technique, and other methods, have been applied successfully to the barrier types of detector (to be described in Chapters 4, 5 and 6,) and there would appear to be no advantage in doing so with bulk counters.

## 2.11   THE SPACE CHARGE DETECTOR

This is described separately from the other types of bulk detector, because it is a special concept likely to be useful only for certain applications. The idea is to utilize the space charge trapping properties of materials, such as cadmium sulphide to provide a simple means of amplifying the signal obtained from the crystal.

A cadmium sulphide gamma flux detector which operates in this way has been developed in the United Kingdom[11]. The excess current (primary and secondary) passed by the crystal is related to the gamma flux and at least $10^9$ electrons are collected per $\gamma$-photon absorbed. The relaxation time is up to 8 sec.

A possible development suggested by D. C. Northrop (private communication), is analogous to the application of photoconductivity described in Chapter 1.11. If a crystal having space charge traps absorbs a single charged particle, there should be no difficulty in collecting the charge supplied by both the primary and the secondary currents so as to obtain an effective gain. *Figure 2.5* illustrates the expected form of the current/time relationship.

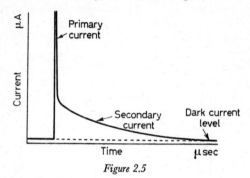

*Figure 2.5*

Cadmium sulphide is an obvious material to try in this application and another possibility is gold-doped silicon, which has already been shown to give secondary currents from charged particles. The counter used by Davies in the experiment described in Chapter 1.5 was erratic but, on occasion, gave a voltage gain of 600, even though the clipping time was too short for full collection. In this crystal the space charge trapping was far from homogeneous and it is probable that this will be the main problem in developing a detector on these lines.

However, it may be easier to make a satisfactory detector for a short pulse of charged particles. If the radiation illuminates the whole volume of the detector any lack of homogeneity will be less important and it may be possible to obtain a consistent relationship between the integrated charge and the total flux. Time resolution would, of course, be poor but in many applications this would be acceptable.

## 2.12 EFFECTS OF RADIATION

The literature on the effects of radiation on semiconductors is very extensive but there appears to have been no work specifically directed to the effects in bulk counters. However, the important effect is that radiation introduces crystal defects and therefore reduces carrier lifetime. Depending on the nature of the defects, it also produces changes in the resistivity; in silicon, for example, $\alpha$-particles, deuterons, neutrons and $\beta$-particles all tend to produce a predominance of deep traps and give increased resistivity[12]. Incidently, this fact suggests that radiation might be used in place of heat treatment to give the deep compensation necessary in the manufacture of bulk counters. The reduction in carrier lifetime caused by radiation and the effect on resistivity will both influence the performance of a bulk counter, but it seems probable that the former will usually be the dominant aging efiect.

Since bulk counters tend to have rather short carrier lifetimes in relation to the collecting time, it is to be expected that their resistance to radiation damage will be poor. Moreover, since their particular virtue for particle counting is the fact that they give linearity up to relatively high energies, it is also to be expected that they will find many of their applications in just those conditions to which they are most vulnerable. It can be confidently predicted that in the near future considerable progress will be made with the lifetime problem and bulk counters will then prove more resistant to radiation effects. For $\gamma$- and $\beta$-radiation a reasonably good detector life may be expected, even with the present materials.

## References

[1] MILLER, G. L., BROWN, W. L., DONOVAN, P. F. and MACKINTOSH, J. M., *Proceedings of Seventh Scintillation Counter Symposium*, Inst. Radio Engrs, N.Y., N.S.7, Nos. 2 and 3 (Sept. 1960) p. 185

[2] JACKSON, R. S., WEBB, P. P. and WILLIAMS, R. L., *Solid State Radiation Detectors*, Inst. Radio Engrs, N.Y., N.S.8, No. 1 (Jan. 1961) p. 29

[3] DAVIS, W. D., *J. appl. Phys.* 29 (1958) 231

[4] VAN PUTTEN, J. D. and VANDER VELDE, J. C., *Solid State Radiation Detectors*, Inst. Radio Engrs, N.Y., N.S.8, No. 1 (Jan. 1961) p. 124

[5] GRIFFITH, R. J., DADDY, C. J., GIBBONS, P. E. and NORTHROP, D. C., *Proceedings of a Conference on Nuclear Electronics* (May 1961), International Atomic Energy Agency

[6] VAN DER ZIEL, A., *Fluctuation Phenomena in Semiconductors*, Butterworths, London (1959)

[7] FAIRSTEIN, E., *Solid State Radiation Detectors*, Inst. Radio Engrs, N.Y., N.S.8, No. 1 (Jan. 1961) p. 129

[8] FONGER, W. H., *Noise in Electrical Devices*, Wiley, New York (1957)

[9] HANSEN, W. and GOULDING, F. S., *Semiconductor Nuclear Particle Detectors*, Nat. Acad. Sci. (Washington), Publ. 871, p. 202

## REFERENCES

[10] DEARNALEY, G. and WHITEHEAD, A. B., *A.E.R.E. Rep.* R-3662 (1961)

[11] *Cadmium Sulphide Crystals as Radiation Detectors*, Harlow Research Laboratory (A.E.I.) (1961)

[12] LARK-HOROVITZ, K. in *Semiconducting Materials* (Ed. H. K. Henisch), Butterworths, London (1951)

[13] SIMPSON, O., *Proceedings of Symposium on Nuclear Instruments, Harwell* 1961 (Ed. by J. B. Birks), Heywood (1962)

# 3

# BARRIER LAYERS AND THEIR PROPERTIES

## 3.1 The *P–N* Junction in Equilibrium

IT IS widely known that samples of semiconductor materials, silicon and germanium in particular, can be obtained which have the following characteristics:

(*a*) The whole sample is one crystal;
(*b*) Part is *P*-type and part is *N*-type;
(*c*) The *P–N* junction occurs at a cross-section of the sample.

Several types of *P–N* junction can be made. This study concerns only very sharp junctions, such as are obtainable by shallow diffusion of impurity and in which the impurity concentration may be approximated by a step function.

An understanding of the properties of such a junction is most readily achieved by thinking of two separate pieces of semiconductor being brought together and joined. The two conduction bands are now in electrical contact, one containing electrons and the other nearly empty. Under the influence of diffusion, electrons flow from the *N* material to the *P* material, as indicated in *Figure 3.1(a)*. The *P*-type crystal therefore acquires a negative charge, and the *N*-type material is positively charged, because it now contains a number of ionized donors whose charges are not balanced by an equal number of free electrons. In the valence band an exactly similar process occurs, some of the holes moving from the *P* material into the *N* material and leaving behind a negative charge due to ionized acceptors. There is, therefore, a transient flow of the majority carriers which establishes a positive charge on the *N* side and an equal negative charge on the *P* side, as indicated in *Figure 3.1(b)*. Such a potential difference (*Q*) does exist across all *P–N* junctions in equilibrium, the magnitude being such that the net flow of carriers across the junction due to diffusion pressure is brought almost to zero by the opposing potential gradient. The reason why, under equilibrium conditions, a small flow of the majority carriers still persists will be explained at the end of this section.

At equilibrium the majority carriers on the two sides of the junction are confined by a potential barrier which they can only cross if they acquire, from chance encounters in thermal diffusion, sufficient kinetic energy. It is shown in most textbooks on the subject that the equilibrium condition is reached when, on an energy scale, the Fermi level is at the same height on the two sides of the junction. This is illustrated in *Figure 3.1(c)*. (To avoid confusion, it should be remem-

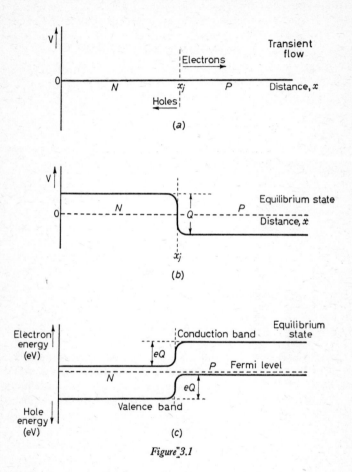

*Figure 3.1*

bered that, when a body acquires a negative charge, the energy of electrons within it is *increased*, and vice versa.) It is seen that electrons moving from the *N* material across the junction face an energy barrier of height *eQ* electron volts. Remembering the convention for the energy of a hole, it is seen that the holes face an equal energy barrier in moving across the junction from the $P$ material. The magnitude of the quantity $eQ$ must, of course, be less than the energy gap, $E_G$.

It is necessary to consider the physical origin of the potential barrier rather more deeply. When such a barrier exists there must be an electric field acting across it, and it follows that there must be parallel layers of electric charge (as on the plates of a condenser) on either side of the barrier. The formation of these charge layers is explained with the help of *Figure 3.2(a)* which shows the concentration of ionized donor centres on a larger scale of abscissae than that of *Figure 3.1*; the concentration of ionized acceptors is shown negative. The larger scale shows a transition zone (A–B) which is assumed to be very small, of the order $10^{-6}$ cm. At equilibrium, when the $P$ side has acquired a

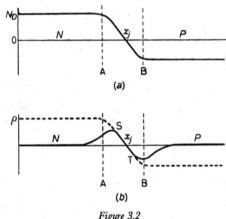

*Figure 3.2*

negative charge relative to the $N$ side, the free majority carriers near the junction are repelled by the charged condition of the material on the other side and therefore withdraw a little, away from the junction

The effect of the repulsion of carriers from the junction is illustrated in *Figure 3.2(b)* in which the ordinates are the local space charge. In the region far to the left of $x_j$ the ionized donors are neutralized by the presence of carrier electrons, so that the space charge is zero. As the junction is approached from the left the concentration of free electrons falls off, due to the repulsion of the negatively charged $P$ zone, and a positive space charge develops in consequence of the excess of ionized donors. At the point $S$ the concentration of carriers has fallen to zero and the space charge curve follows the curve of impurity centres through the transition zone to $T$. A similar argument explains the shape of the space charge curve in the $P$ region, and the charge layers referred to earlier are seen in the maximum and minimum near $S$ and $T$ respectively.

The important consequence of this is illustrated in *Figure 3.3*, which shows the concentration of carriers. There is a small region on either side of $x_j$ which is depleted of carriers; this is called the 'depletion region' or 'depletion zone'. It should be noted that the depletion zone does *not* coincide with the transition region.

In the foregoing paragraphs attention has been directed exclusively to the behaviour of the majority carriers. It is now necessary to consider what happens to the minority carriers. There are a few holes on the $N$ side and these are subject to diffusion, so that some are continually wandering towards the junction. Unlike the electrons, these minority carriers are attracted by the negative charge on the $P$ side, and as soon as they come under the influence of the field across

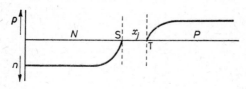

Figure 3.3

the junction region they accelerate and cross it. For similar reasons there is a small continuous flow of electrons from the $P$ to the $N$ side. This dual flow constitutes a 'drift' current flowing from the $N$ side to the $P$ side (down the gradient of potential) which is proportional to the area of the junction. Its value, per unit area, is denoted by '$I_s$', where

$$I_s = I_{s.p} + I_{s.n} \qquad \ldots (3.1)$$

There is also another source of current from the $N$ to the $P$ side, due to the fact that processes of carrier generation continue in the depletion zone, the carriers being swept out by the field as soon as they are formed. This current depends on the generation rate and is proportional to the volume of the zone. If $I_G$ is its value per unit area of the cross-section,

$$I_G = 2g.Xq \qquad \ldots (3.2)$$

where $g$ is the generation rate of carriers and $X$ is the barrier width (the width of the depletion zone).

At equilibrium, the flow of minority carriers, in accordance with the above equations, is balanced by an equal flow of majority carriers in opposite directions. This is the residual 'diffusion current' mentioned at the beginning of this section, and arises from a small proportion of majority carriers which acquire sufficient thermal energy to cross the barriers of *Figure 3.1(c)*. Therefore,

$$|I_f| = I_s + I_G \qquad \qquad \ldots (3.3)$$

At ordinary temperatures, with most semiconductors, all these currents, particularly $I_G$, are very small, of the order $10^{-9} \text{A}/\text{cm}^2$ or less. In this condition of equilibrium the depletion zone is very small, consequently, $I_G$ is small compared with $I_s$. It is therefore sufficiently accurate for all practical purposes to write

$$|I_f| = I_s \qquad \qquad \ldots (3.3a)$$

## 3.2   The *P–N* Junction with Applied Potential

The height of the potential barrier illustrated in *Figure 3.1* can be altered by connecting the two sides of the junction to an external e.m.f. Let the applied change in potential be $V$, and let it be measured according to the amount by which the potential of the $P$ side is increased or decreased in relation to that of the $N$ side. The effect on the potential barrier is illustrated in *Figure 3.4*.

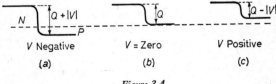

V Negative          V = Zero          V Positive

(a)                    (b)                  (c)

Figure 3.4

The result of this, in qualitative terms, can readily be understood by reference to the previous section and to the simple formulae of the above three equations. Considering, first, case (a), the drift current will not be affected by the increased height of the barrier, since it will still be determined solely by the rate at which the minority carriers wander into the barrier region. $I_s$ is therefore unaltered. It is shown later, and in Appendix C, that the carrier generation current (negligible when $V$ is zero) increases when $V$ is negative and then becomes significant. For this purpose it is sufficient to denote the new value by the symbol $I_G'$. The total current flowing down the gradient of potential is, therefore, $I_s + I_G'$.

Under these conditions the diffusion current is reduced in consequence of the increase in the height of the barrier, and therefore decreases to some new value $I'_f$. The balance of current expressed in eqn. (3.3) is therefore destroyed and there is a net current flow in the direction of the applied p.d. (from the $N$ side to the $P$ side) given by

$$I_r = I_s + I'_G - |I'_f| \qquad \ldots (3.4)$$

This current is termed the 'reverse current' because it is associated with reverse bias (negative $V$). If $V$ increases to more than a few volts, $I'_f$ becomes zero and thereafter $I_r$ increases only very slightly as the negative bias, $V$, increases. This is the basis of the rectifying property of a $P-N$ junction, which is described in greater detail in the next paragraph.

It has already been explained (Chapter 1.5) that the carrier energy distributions follow the classical law and therefore, for majority carriers, the concentration of carriers having sufficient energy to surmount a potential barrier of height $E_B$ is proportional to $\exp(-E_B/kT)$. The height of a potential barrier in energy units is the product of the electronic charge and the numerical value of the potential difference. Therefore,

$$E_B = (Q + |V|) q = (Q - V) q$$

and

$$I'_f = I_f \frac{e^{-(Q-V)q/kT}}{e^{-Qq/kT}} = I_f e^{Vq/kT} \quad (V \text{ is negative})$$

Substituting for $I_f$, from eqn. (3.3a),

$$I'_f = |I_s| e^{Vq/kT}$$

Therefore, from eqn. (3.4),

$$I_r = I_s (1 - e^{Vq/kT}) + I'_G \qquad \ldots (3.5)$$

When the negative bias exceeds one or two volts the exponential term disappears.

If the reverse current is regarded as negative (3.5) may be written

$$I = I_s (e^{Vq/kT} - 1) - I'_G \qquad \ldots (3.5a)$$

When the applied potential is positive, as in case (c), $I_s$ again remains constant and $I_G$ remains at a negligibly low level. The diffusion current, however, is increased because the potential barrier is reduced. A repetition of the same deductions leads to the conclusion that 'forward' current also obeys the law (3.5a), but the current and $V$ are now positive and $I'_G$ is zero.

The relationship in (3.5a) is shown in *Figure 3.5* which illustrates the performance of a $P-N$ junction as a rectifier. Such 'junction diodes' are widely used in transistorized electronic circuits. The reverse current shown on the left of the diagram does not quite limit; there is a small increase in the region $-1$ to $-30$ V, due to the generation current.

Much of the literature on the electrical properties of $P$–$N$ junctions relates to rectifying devices, or junction diodes, as used in electronic circuits. Such junctions are made from material having very much lower bulk resistivity than that used in semiconductor counters and their properties differ in several respects. For example, $I'_G$ gives a negligible contribution to the reverse current in a junction diode and

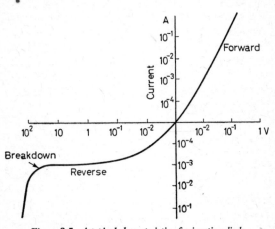

Figure 3.5. *A typical characteristic of a junction diode*

does not usually appear in the equation of the current voltage characteristic, whereas in a junction detector $I'_G$ is nearly always greater than the $I_s$ term. It is generally necessary to be cautious in applying conclusions based on a study of junction diodes to problems relating to detectors.

Only the reverse characteristic is of interest in connexion with particle detectors and the above formula is therefore used in the form of eqn. (3.5), the direction of the reverse current being taken for granted. The theory of the reverse current is described in more detail in Appendix C, where it is explained that there is an additional component, not mentioned above, due to leakage. This current, $I_L$, also flows in the direction of the applied potential difference and owes its existence to the fact that the rectifying barrier does not extend right to the surface of the crystal and surface conductivity (see Chapter 1.12) therefore permits leakage all round the perimeter of the barrier layer. In Appendix C, $I_s$ and $I'_G$ are evaluated in terms of the properties of the crystal; $I_L$ is mathematically intractable and depends very much on the condition of the surfaces concerned.

## 3.3 THE BARRIER WIDTH

The condition of interest for particle detection is that of reverse bias, in which the junction has a high resistance. By reason of the applied potential the barrier has been increased in height and the two charge layers referred to in Chapter 3.1 are necessarily intensified. Referring to *Figure 3.2(b)*, it is seen that the magnitudes at S and T of the space charge concentration are limited by the concentrations of donor and acceptor centres; the increase in total space charge can therefore only be brought about by an increase in the depth of the two layers. This is shown in *Figure 3.6*, which should be compared with *Figure 3.2(b)*.

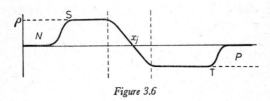

*Figure 3.6*

To put this in another way, the majority carriers retreat further from the junction and leave a larger depletion zone on either side of the point $x_j$, see *Figure 3.7*. Note that the barrier depth is not symmetrical about $x_j$, the asymmetry being dependent on the net impurity concentrations.

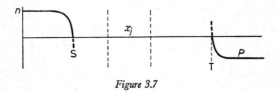

*Figure 3.7*

The width of the depletion zone therefore increases as the applied reverse bias is increased and the process can be continued until the junction breaks down. In ordinary junctions the depletion zone can have widths from a few microns up to about 0·08 cm. It is important to appreciate that the effective resistance of the depletion zone is, in general, greater by many orders of magnitude than the bulk resistivity of the material on either side of the junction. Practically the whole of any applied bias therefore appears as the potential difference $(V)$ across the barrier region and the electric field may rise to about $10^4$ V/cm.

Referring back to the statement of desirable characteristics of a material for a crystal detector, in Chapter 1.13, it can now be appreciated that the barrier region of a semiconductor junction under reverse bias meets at least some of the requirements almost perfectly. There is a zone of crystalline material of finite dimensions; it is subject to a high potential gradient, but the current flow across it is very small. This region is radiation-sensitive.

Particle detectors which utilize the barrier layer formed at a junction under reverse bias are of two main types, called 'diffused junction' and 'surface barrier' detectors, respectively. They differ in their construction but are very similar in their properties and their performance. The next two chapters are devoted to these two types separately, describing their construction and the differences between them. Then follows a chapter in which the two are discussed together under a general heading. It is, perhaps, desirable to point out here that the possibilities of barrier layer detection are not limited to devices which fall into one or other of these classes; a modification which is already the subject of experiment will be described in Chapter 7 and other methods of obtaining suitable barriers may later be found.

# 4

# BARRIER LAYER DETECTORS:
# DIFFUSED JUNCTION TYPE

## 4.1 INTRODUCTION

A DIFFUSED junction detector is a semiconductor crystal having a junction formed very close to one of its surfaces by diffusing atoms of an impurity into that face, thus overcompensating the impurity already present and producing a thin inversion layer. For the sake of brevity, and following the practice of other writers, the name is shortened to 'junction detectors' in most of the text. Nearly all such detectors so far made have been in $P$-type silicon (fully described here as '$P$–$N$ silicon diffused junction detectors') and most of this chapter is therefore devoted to this material.

The first reported detection of charged particles using a semi-conductor junction appears to be the work of McKay[1] in 1949 on $\alpha$-particles. He used a 'grown' junction and the particles entered the barrier region in a direction parallel to the plane of the junction. This, of course, results in a device having a very small aperture, and the use of diffusion to form a junction very close to one surface overcomes this problem, enabling particles to be detected which enter through the surface inversion layer. Techniques for producing satisfactory diffused junctions on silicon have been worked out by several groups in the United States, the United Kingdom and France.

## 4.2 DESCRIPTION

A silicon $P$–$N$ junction detector has the following properties (see *Figures 4.1.* and *4.2*):

(a) Practically the whole volume is a single crystal of high resistivity $P$-type silicon of high perfection, so that trapping is a minimum.

(b) The junction lies within one micron or less of one face and is very abrupt.

(c) The $N$ material is lightly doped at the junction but the donor concentration rises very rapidly, so that the surface conductivity on that face is relatively very high. This eliminates the need for a metallic electrode and contact is usually made near the edge of this surface, leaving a central area exposed. This is the aperture through which radiation enters.

(*d*) The junction is operated under reverse bias, the *N* material being made positive. Under these conditions of heavy surface doping the contact at the *N* face is of relatively low resistance.

(*e*) The contact to the *P* material is by an ohmic contact to a metal electrode at the opposite face. Almost the whole of the applied potential therefore appears across the depletion zone at the junction.

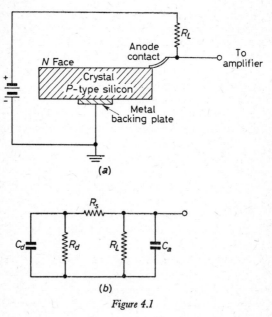

Figure 4.1

*Figure 4.1(a)* illustrates a typical *P–N* silicon junction detector, with a diagrammatic representation of the electrical connexions made when in use. The cross-section may be circular or rectangular and the width may vary from approximately 1 mm to 2 cm. There are advantages in having only a moderate thickness and this is not usually much in excess of 1 mm. *Figure 4.1(b)* shows the circuit with the addition of crystal impedances ($C_d$ and $R_d$) and the amplifier input capacitance ($C_a$). $R_s$ is the resistance of the bulk of the crystal, outside the depletion zone, plus that of the electrodes and their contacts.

*Figure 4.2(a)* shows the barrier, or depletion zone, near the *N* face of the crystal. The junction should be less than 1 $\mu$ from the surface and is commonly no more than $\frac{1}{2}\,\mu$ deep. *Figure 4.2(b)* shows the space charge concentrations. It has already been explained (Chapters 3.1 and 3.3) that the space charges are equal and the $N$ and $P$ parts of the depletion zone are therefore of widths depending inversely on the net concentrations of donor and acceptor centres, respectively. In this detector $N_D$ rises rapidly to a value many orders of magnitude greater than $N_A$, and $x_p$ is commonly about 1,000 times $x_n$. Consequently, the barrier is, for all practical purposes, entirely in the $P$ material.

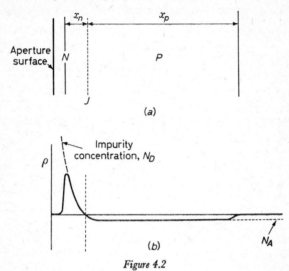

Figure 4.2

The choice of silicon for most junction detectors has been dictated by the fact that good quality $P$-type silicon crystals of high resistivity can be obtained and an $N$-type surface can readily be obtained by diffusion of a suitable impurity. The technique of obtaining an abrupt junction close to the surface and heavy surface doping is relatively well established for $P$ silicon. An additional factor is the intrinsic conductivity, which is low enough to enable junction detectors to be operated at ambient temperatures.

Germanium has appreciable intrinsic conductivity at ambient temperatures and detectors made from it require to be cooled, usually by liquid air or nitrogen. In some applications this is advantageous and, at low temperatures, germanium is in certain respects superior to silicon. McKay used germanium $N$–$P$ junctions in his early experiment to determine the energy absorbed per ion pair.

Junction detectors are susceptible to contamination by the ambient atmosphere. Not only does moisture affect the side faces, giving

59

increased reverse current due to surface leakage, but other contaminants may enter the crystal and modify its behaviour. Counters are best stored in a desiccator, or preferably, *in vacuo*[2].

## 4.3 METHOD OF PREPARATION

The detailed procedure for making a junction detector is by no means stereotyped, each worker employing his own methods. The following method is described here by courtesy of Dr. D. C. Northrop and is constantly being varied as improvements are found. Another method is described by Donovan[2].

*Silicon P–N Junction Detector: Method of Preparation*

The starting material is *P*-type silicon of minority carrier lifetime about 1 msec. This is cut to a suitable cross-section, depending on the counter size required, and sliced to a thickness of about 1 mm. It is ground and lapped on all surfaces.

The crystal is etched in C.P.4 (or 80:20 nitric and hydrofluoric acids) at 40–50° C, following the procedure described for bulk detectors in Chapter 2.6.

One face is uniformly coated with phosphorus pentoxide dissolved in ethylene glycol (2:10 by volume) and diffusion is carried out by heating at 800° C in dry nitrogen for half an hour. This is about the lowest time and temperature which is found to give reproducible results. The resistivity increases by about 5–10 per cent and the lifetime is reduced by about half, to 500 μsec approximately.

The diffused surface is protected with Apiezon wax and the sides and opposite face are etched at 40–50° C for about half an hour. The crystal is washed and the wax dissolved away in toluene in an ultrasonic bath. The toluene is removed with alcohol and the crystal is dried.

The back contact is made by alloying at 400° C on to a gold plate, the gold containing about 1 per cent of boron. The plate need have only a small area, thus reducing problems arising from different coefficients of thermal expansion.

Connexion is made to the active surface by means of a gold wire secured with FSP43 or 49 (at 100° C), or with silver paste, X351 at 400° C.

High resistivity silicon of good, uniform quality is not easy to obtain and it is usual to find that a proportion of the detectors made are unsatisfactory, due to crystal defects. Inhomogeneity, particularly local areas of very low carrier lifetime, appears to be the main problem. Among counters which may be classed as 'successful', energy resolution differs appreciably from unit to unit and a really first-grade counter, giving resolution approaching 0·3 per cent on α-particles, can only be obtained by selection from a group. There is every reason to expect improved consistency from the development of techniques for refining silicon in the course of the next few years.

## 4.4  PRINCIPLES OF OPERATION

The production of a pair of carriers (electron plus hole) involves the absorption of 3·6 eV in silicon, and about 3·0 eV in germanium, on the average. A 10 MeV particle therefore creates $2·8 \times 10^6$ carrier pairs (or $3·3 \times 10^6$ in germanium) which are initially distributed along the track of the particle, and then move under the influence of the applied field. The number of carriers produced is closely proportional to the energy lost and independent of the nature of the particle; the detector can, therefore, give excellent linearity with energy, provided all the carriers are collected.

Since the conductivity in the surface layer, and even that in the bulk of the $P$-type crystal, are both vastly greater than in the depletion zone, the boundaries of the zone act as the electrodes. The sensitive volume is much smaller in depth than in the case of a bulk detector and may range in practical cases from about 10 or 20 μ to 0·8 mm. As in the case of the bulk detector, strict proportionality requires a time constant large enough to obtain almost complete collection. In addition, proportionality is only obtained if (*a*) the insensitive surface $N$ layer is negligible, and (*b*) the zone depth is sufficient to stop all particles concerned. The second requirement imposes limits on linearity with energy for different particles, as shown in the table below.

TABLE 4.1. APPROXIMATE LIMITS OF ENERGY PROPORTIONALITY
(ZONE DEPTH 0·8 mm)

| | |
|---|---|
| Protons | 11 MeV |
| Deuterons | 14 MeV |
| Tritons | 16 MeV |
| α-particles | 45 MeV |
| Helium[3] ions | 40 MeV |

The reverse current, even at high bias, is only $\mu A/cm^2$ and therefore no problems of overheating arise. Noise increases with reverse current and often limits the bias which can be applied, but a limit is also imposed by the onset of breakdown. This limit varies over a wide range but an average value is about 300–400 V for silicon and about 50–100 V for germanium. As an indication of the wide variation it may be mentioned that a bias of 2,000 V has been applied[3] without break-down across a silicon junction of area 50 mm$^2$. The electric field across the barrier is not uniform, but the average over the zone is of the order $10^3$ V/cm. This very high field, coupled with the small distances involved, gives collecting times of the order $10^{-9}$ sec.

Pulse height is of the order of millivolts and is determined, for a given particle energy, by the total capacitance in the circuit. Although the detector capacitance is higher than that of a bulk detector it does not seriously limit the pulse height. Exceptions to this arise when operating with particles of low energy using very thin sensitive zones, The limit of low energy resolution, however, is usually imposed by noise. A typical detector capacitance would be of the order of 50 pF.

Junction detectors are photosensitive and, in fact, were used as photocells before their possibilities as particle detectors were realized. They must, therefore, be used in darkness.

Despite the differences in geometry, the problems of charge collection are similar to those of a bulk detector. However, there are now always some holes which must make the full transit across the barrier and, therefore, the collecting time is more nearly constant for various particle tracks and is always equal to the total transit time. Since collection is collinear with the particle track ambipolar effects (see Chapter 2.4) are likely to be greater. Moreover, there is evidence[4] that some recombination occurs due to the very high density of carriers moving axially through the column of 'plasma' left by the particle. However, even with this geometry, neither the ambipolar effect nor the 'columnar recombination' are significant for ordinary purposes; they have been detected only with fission fragments.

In a junction detector (and in any barrier layer detector) the depletion zone cannot have excess carriers injected into it from either of its boundaries. Under reverse bias the potential gradient opposes the flow of electrons from the $N$ side and of holes from the $P$ side. Consequently, the phenomenon described in Chapter 1.11, cannot occur; even in the presence of space charge effects there is no secondary current. Space charge trapping in junction detectors has no effect other than that of reducing the primary current and causing incomplete collection.

## 4.5 THE DEPLETION ZONE

It is shown in Appendix C that in such junctions as that of a detector, where $N_D \gg N_A$, the barrier depth, $X$, is given approximately by the equation

$$X = \left(\frac{\epsilon V}{2\pi q N}\right)^{\frac{1}{2}} \qquad \dots (4.1)$$

where $\epsilon$ is the dielectric constant of the material, $V$ the reverse bias, $q$ the electronic charge and $N$ ($= N_A$) the net concentration of acceptor centres, all in c.g.s. units. The depletion zone is the sensitive volume and one very advantageous feature is that its depth can be altered, within limits, simply by changing the applied bias, $V$. It should be noted that eqn. (4.1) is derived on the assumption that the impurity centres are fully ionized. As long as this condition is met, the barrier depth does not vary appreciably with temperature.

A limit on zone adjustment by bias voltage is imposed by the onset of breakdown or by noise, and further increase in $X$ can then be obtained by reducing $N$ to a minimum [see eqn. (4.1)]. As in the case of bulk detectors, the problem of carrier lifetime is an important factor, but, since the sensitive zone is smaller by an order of magnitude and the electric field is also greater, there is a better margin. Further-more, the high lifetime in the original crystal can be better preserved because it is unnecessary to use such high temperatures in preparation. Detectors with a zone depth of 0·8 mm, equal to the range of an 11 MeV proton, can be obtained with 12,000 $\Omega$cm uncompensated silicon. Such material, however, is at present very difficult to obtain.

A junction is, in effect, a layer of high resistance material separating opposite electric charges and consequently has appreciable capacit-ance, which varies with $X$ and therefore with $V$. The effective capacitance per square centimetre is given approximately by

$$C_d = \frac{\epsilon}{4\pi X} \quad \text{(e.s.u.)} \qquad \ldots (4.2)$$

From eqn. (4.1)

$$C_d = \frac{1}{2}\left(\frac{\epsilon q N}{2\pi V}\right)^{\frac{1}{2}} \quad \text{(e.s.u.)} \qquad \ldots (4.2a)$$

Capacitance is best measured by operating the detector with mono-energetic particles and observing the effect on pulse height when a known capacitance is connected in parallel. This has the advantage that the measurement is made under appropriate dynamic conditions. From eqn. (4.2), the capacitance should be inversely proportional to the square root of the applied bias (more correctly, $V$ should include the small contact potential which is present in the absence of bias). In practice it is found that

$$C_d \propto V^{-r}$$

where $r$ is often somewhat less than 0·5. The discrepancy is attributed to the junction not being abrupt, so that the transition zone con-tributes appreciably to the width of the depletion zone, and gives reduced capacitance for a given applied bias.

Measurements[5] of capacitance of two junction counters showed $r = 0.39$ and $0.35$. On the other hand, it is to be inferred that junctions with $r$ very close to $0.5$ can be made[6]. The precise value of $r$ does not materially affect the performance of the counter, but it may be argued that a low value could be slightly advantageous by giving a marginal increase in the depth of the sensitive volume.

For calculations, eqn. (4.1) can be expressed in more suitable terms. By eqn. (1.7b)

$$qN\mu = \sigma = \frac{1}{\rho}$$

where $\rho$ is the resistivity of the parent crystal and $\mu$ is the mobility of the majority carriers. Substituting for $qN$ and converting to practical units, with $V$ in volts, $\mu$ in $cm^2/V\,sec$ and $\rho$ in $\Omega\,cm$,

$$X = 4.2 \times 10^{-7}\,(\epsilon V\rho\mu)^{\frac{1}{3}}\,cm \qquad \ldots (4.1b)$$

Values of $\rho$ and $\mu$ used in this equation must of course, be consistent in the sense that they refer to the same temperature; furthermore, the temperature concerned must be such that the impurity centres are fully ionized.

The electric field in the depletion zone is not uniform, the law being determined by Poisson's equation,

$$\frac{d^2\phi}{dx^2} = -\frac{4\pi qN}{\epsilon} \quad \text{(e.s.u.)} \qquad \ldots (4.3)$$

where $\phi$ is the potential at a point defined by the position coordinate, $x$. From this, the electric field in the $P$ region (where $N$ is constant) is

$$F = \frac{d\phi}{dx} = -\frac{4\pi qN}{\epsilon}\,x + \text{const.} \qquad \ldots (4.4)$$

If $x$ is taken arbitrarily as zero at the junction, with its positive axis extending into the $P$ region, the boundary condition is that $F$ must be zero when $x = x_p$ (see *Figure 4.2*). From this the constant of eqn. (4.4) can be evaluated and

$$F = \frac{4\pi qN}{\epsilon}\,(x_p - x) \qquad \ldots (4.4a)$$

But $x_p$ is very nearly equal to the whole barrier depth and therefore, without appreciable error,

$$F = \frac{4\pi qN}{\epsilon}\,(X - x) \qquad \ldots (4.4b)$$

64

The field strength is therefore a maximum near the junction ($x = 0$) and decreases linearly to zero at the edge of the depletion zone. The maximum value is obtained by substituting for $X$ from eqn. (4.1) and is found to be

$$F \text{ max.} = \sqrt{\left(\frac{8\pi qNV}{\epsilon}\right)} \qquad \ldots (4.5)$$

At high bias volts in a typical counter, $F$ max. is of the order $10^4$ V/cm.
From eqns. (4.4) and (4.4b),

$$d\phi = \frac{4\pi qN}{\epsilon}(X - x)\,dx$$

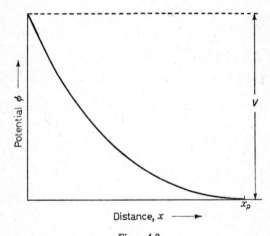

Figure 4.3

Integrating over the range $x = 0$ to $x = x_p = X$ gives the potential drop across the barrier,

$$[\phi]_0^X = \frac{4\pi qN}{\epsilon}\left[Xx - \frac{x^2}{2}\right]_0^X = \frac{4\pi qN}{\epsilon}\cdot\frac{X^2}{2} = V \quad \text{[by eqn. (4.1)]}$$
$$\ldots (4.6)$$

Therefore, with these approximations (neglecting $x_n$) all the potential drop occurs in the $P$ material and is equal to the applied bias. The fall of potential is quadratic and is illustrated in *Figure 4.3*.

Equation (4.5) suggests that the use of high resistivity material ($N$ low) would reduce the maximum field strength and permit the application of high bias volts without breakdown. This particular

65

advantage, however, is only partially realized in practice, since breakdown appears to be initiated by surface leakage current in the periphery of the depletion zone.

Blankenship[7] has produced a nomograph from eqns. (4.1) and (4.2) using data appropriate to silicon at ambient temperatures. This is reproduced in Appendix A and shows that in a sample of *P*-type silicon of resistivity about 9,500 $\Omega$ cm (which would be classed as very high) a bias of nearly 300 V would be needed to give a depletion zone

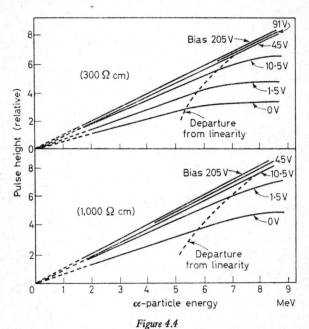

*Figure 4.4*

(S. S. Friedland, J. W. Mayer and J. S. Wiggins[5], 'Reprinted from *Nucleonics*, 18, No. 2, p. 58. Copyright 1960, McGraw-Hill Publishing Company, Inc.)'

of 0·5 mm. The greatest resistivity for silicon reported in the literature is 12,000 $\Omega$ cm, with a similar bias this would give a zone depth of 0·6 mm, according to these simple equations.

Measurements of zone depth are made either by measuring the capacitance as described earlier, or by determining the limit of linear response to particles of increasing energy and known penetration. Some results of the latter are illustrated in *Figure 4.4*[5].

The depth of the sensitive zone, as measured by known particle energies, is generally rather greater than the calculated value given by Blankenship's nomograph. For example, the above diagrams show linearity for $\alpha$-particles up to 6·5 and 8 MeV at 10·5 V bias in 300 $\Omega$ and 1,000 $\Omega$ $P$-type silicon respectively. Blankenship's nomograph predicts linearity only up to 4·5 and 6·4 MeV, respectively. Many similar discrepancies can be found from the literature and are hardly surprising in view of the simplifying assumptions used in the theory. The explanation lies in the fact that the boundary of the depletion zone is diffuse, there being a concentration gradient of carriers extending to about the diffusion length beyond its theoretical limit. Also, of course, there is a small potential gradient. For both these reasons minority carriers formed outside the depletion zone do move slowly towards it and will be collected if they survive long enough.

These considerations suggest that 99 per cent collection will be obtained in a region of depth '$s$' beyond the depletion zone, where $s$ is some small fraction of the diffusion length and will vary with the resistivity of the base material and the applied bias. It appears that, very approximately,

$$s \sim 0\cdot 1 L$$

where $L$ is the diffusion length of the minority carriers and may range in practical cases from about 0·03 to 0·7 mm. This 'bonus' on the sensitive volume is worth noting, and from eqn. (1.9) it is to be expected that a high diffusion coefficient will contribute appreciably.

To avoid possible confusion, the region of crystal over which linearity can be obtained (the sensitive volume of the detector) will be referred to as the 'sensitive zone' or the 'barrier region'. The term 'depletion zone' will be used when referring to the region of very low carrier concentration.

### 4.6 PULSE HEIGHT AND PROPORTIONALITY

The charge released is closely proportional to the energy absorbed within the sensitive zone and is independent of the nature of the particle. For silicon the number of ion pairs per MeV is $2\cdot 8 \times 10^5$ and for germanium $3\cdot 3 \times 10^5$; the charge released per MeV is therefore 4·4 and $5\cdot 6 \times 10^{-14}$ C, respectively. On the assumption of full collection the pulse height is

$$P = \frac{Q}{C_d + C_a} \qquad \ldots (4.7)$$

where $C_a$ is the input capacitance of the amplifier plus stray capacitance. Now, $C_d$ varies with the barrier depth and therefore with the

6                 67

applied bias; consequently, rigid proportionality $(P \propto Q)$ will only be obtained if

$$C_a \geqslant C_d$$

or if $C_d = $ const., i.e. the bias is kept constant.

The requirements for maximum pulse height (small capacitance) conflict, therefore, with those for linearity and with those for good time resolution ($X$ small, subject to being greater than the penetration, and $C_d$ therefore large). The optimum conditions are a matter of compromise, depending on the primary object. With ordinary amplifiers and appreciable barrier depth, $C_a$ will often be dominant.

Reference to Blankenship's nomograph shows the detector capacitance per unit area varying between 10 and 1,000 pF, according to resistivity and the bias applied. For an average counter, having an area of about 10 mm$^2$, the range would be from 1 to 100 pF and with a reasonably deep barrier it would be about 5 to 30 pF. With a total capacitance of 200 pF eqn. (4.7) gives a pulse height about 0·2 mV per MeV.

With a special counter of large aperture (1 or 2 cm$^2$) the situation is entirely different. Counter capacitance is likely to be dominant; pulse heights would be only about 0·1 mV per MeV and would vary considerably with applied bias. This, however, can be overcome by the use of a charge sensitive pre-amplifier (Chapter 9.3).

For good proportionality it is essential that the 'window' thickness be negligible; this is the highly doped layer between the surface and the depletion zone. Holes generated in this region would be expected to have a very small chance of reaching the sensitive zone, and being collected, partly because the electric field is negligible but mainly because the intense doping results in heavy trapping and a very short lifetime. The reduction of the window to a minimum is a very important factor in the manufacture of junction detectors and it is fortunate that techniques have been developed which are proving remarkably successful. A counter with a window exceeding 1 μ would be considered poor by current standards and a thickness of 0·1 μ has been claimed[8]. It is also claimed that such very thin conducting layers do not actually constitute a window at all, because hole lifetime remains great enough to enable efficient collection to occur by diffusion over such short distances.

In practice it can reasonably be claimed that the window problem has been solved†. The effect should be most noticeable for heavy particles of small penetration, but an analysis of the $^{252}$Cf fission spectrum with a good counter showed no apparent window[8]. It is also

† See Chapter 10.4.

reported[5] that good linearity for $\alpha$-particles can be obtained down to 0·3 MeV, which argues a window much less than 0·2 $\mu$. Jackson *et al.*[9] report experiments on the photosensitivity of detectors which confirmed the absence of any significant window.

## 4.7   COLLECTING TIME

If $\mu_p < \mu_n$, the full collecting time in a $P$-type ($P$–$N$) detector is the same for particles of all energies, because there are always some holes which make the full transit. This time can be calculated approximately from the known law of field strength in the barrier layer and the drift mobility for the slower carriers. Starting from eqn. (4.4b)

$$F = \frac{4\pi qN}{\epsilon} (X-x) \qquad \ldots (4.4b)$$

put the coefficient, 

$$\frac{4\pi qN}{\epsilon} = a$$

then 

$$F = a(X-x)$$

Now, $\quad v_d = \dfrac{dx}{dt} = \mu F,\quad$ (where $\mu$ is the hole mobility, $\mu_p$)

therefore 

$$dt = \frac{1}{\mu} \cdot \frac{dx}{F} = \frac{1}{\mu a} \cdot \frac{dx}{(X-x)}$$

and 

$$t = \frac{1}{\mu a} \int \frac{dx}{(X-x)}$$

Hence 

$$t(x) = \frac{1}{\mu a} [-\ln(X-x)]_{x=0}^{x}$$

If the integration is carried out over the full theoretical width of the depletion zone the result is infinite. This arises from the assumed boundary condition that $F = $ zero when $x = X$ and is obviously unreal. To obtain a rational result it is necessary to assume that collection is complete when the slowest carriers (holes) originating near the crystal surface have almost crossed the depletion zone. The integration is therefore taken to the limit $x = kX$, where $k$ is a fraction slightly less than unity. On this basis,

$$t_c = \frac{1}{\mu a} (\ln X - \ln(1-k)X) = \frac{1}{\mu a} \cdot \ln \frac{1}{1-k} \qquad \ldots (4.8)$$

If $k$ is 0·99,
$$\ln\left(\frac{1}{1-k}\right) = 4·6$$

Therefore
$$t_c = \frac{4·6}{\mu a} = \frac{4·6\,\epsilon}{4\pi q N \mu} \qquad \ldots (4.9)$$

It must be emphasized that this is a simple estimate, suitable only for very approximate calculations. The theory on which it is based makes a very rough approximation in the integration and does not distinguish between the depletion zone and the actual barrier layer. Furthermore, no allowance is made for ambipolar effect (see 2.4) nor is any allowance made for the reduced carrier mobility in a high field (see 1.7).

However, it is of interest that the collecting time is approximately independent of applied bias and depth of barrier layer. This confers upon the $P$-type junction detector the useful advantage that the decay constant does not require readjustment as the bias is altered. Also, a suitable decay constant will give a similar time resolution for each particle of a mixed flux, provided that all are stopped within the barrier layer.

Reverting to eqn. (4.9), it may be assumed without appreciable error that the acceptor centres are completely ionized, so that $N = p$ (the concentration of holes in the parent crystal) and the concentration of electron carriers may be neglected. In this case the product

$$qN\mu = qp\mu_p = \frac{1}{\rho}$$

where $\rho$ is the resistivity of the parent crystal.

Making this substitution gives
$$t_c = \frac{4·6\,\epsilon\rho}{4\pi} \qquad \ldots (4.9a)$$

Converting this from electrostatic units to practical units, if $\rho$ is measured in $\Omega\,$cm the collecting time is

$$t_c = \frac{\epsilon\rho}{8\pi}\,10^{-11}\text{ sec, approx.} \qquad \ldots (4.9b)$$

Because of the uneven distribution of carriers, and the fact that collection is collinear with the particle track, it is difficult to calculate the form of the leading edge of the pulse in terms of the rate of accumulation of charge. Moreover, any such calculation would still give only an approximate estimate of the pulse rise time according to the convention usually employed (10 to 90 per cent) because the shape of the leading edge is modified by transmission of the voltage pulse through those parts of the crystal other than the depletion layer, which have appreciable impedance. To obtain the shortest possible pulse rise time the series resistance of the crystal ($R_s$ of *Figure 4.1*) should be cut to a minimum by having a total crystal thickness only very little more than is necessary to accommodate the deepest barrier layer likely to be employed.† However, for reasons to be explained at the end of Chapter 4.8, it is generally best to ensure that the barrier layer does not penetrate right through to the back contact.

A silicon $P$-type detector in 1,000 $\Omega$ cm crystal at ambient temperature would give a collecting time, according to eqn. (4.9), of about $5 \times 10^{-9}$ sec. If a calculation is done for a case in which the carriers are initially evenly distributed across the whole depletion zone, it is found that the rise time (10 to 90 per cent )would be about one-quarter of this figure, $1 \cdot 3 \times 10^{-9}$ sec, and the actual distribution of excess carriers would favour a rise time even shorter. Such small rise times are, of course, unlikely to be realized fully in practice because of ambipolar effect and the series impedance, but the indications are that the above calculations are not unduly optimistic for particles of moderate energy. In any event, the limit of possible time resolution is determined by the electronics. In detecting fission fragments collecting times are found[10] to be significantly longer than the theoretical figure and this is attributed to ambipolar effect arising from the very considerable density of carriers along the particle track.

These calculations show that if good collection (and good energy resolution) is required, the carrier lifetime should not be less than about $10^{-7}$ sec in 1,000 $\Omega$ crystal. Long lifetime is more important in material of high resistivity. With silicon and germanium counters it is possible to have lifetimes of the order $10^{-4}$ sec, but it is not easy to obtain adequate uniformity.

## 4.8   REVERSE CURRENT

The steady current passed by the detector in the absence of radiation is termed 'reverse' current (from its association with the reverse bias) or 'dark' current. The theory of reverse current has already been touched on in Chapter 3.2, and further details are described in Appendix C. In a junction detector the reverse current is always small (a few microamps at most) and is of no significance as far as the heating effect is concerned. It is, however, an important factor in the operation of a detector because it can be the main source of noise in the system and may limit resolution.

† See Chapter 10.7.

The reverse current across a junction has three components (see 3.2):

(a) the drift current due to diffusion of minority carriers into the depletion zone, $I_s$;

(b) the carrier generation current, due to carriers produced by thermal generation in the depletion zone, $I_G'$;

(c) the surface leakage current, $I_L$.

The first two involve a flow of current through the bulk of the crystal and are, therefore, proportional to cross-section. The third is a flow through the surface layer (by-passing the depletion zone) which is proportional to the perimeter of the crystal.

The drift current (a) has two components, one due to the diffusion of holes from the $N$ side and the other due to diffusion of electrons from the $P$ side; its value, per unit area of cross-section (see Appendix C) is:

$$I_s = q^{\frac{3}{2}} n_i^2 \sqrt{(\mu_p . \mu_n . kT)} \left( \frac{\mu_p^{\frac{1}{2}} \rho_p}{\tau_n^{\frac{1}{2}}} + \frac{\mu_n^{\frac{1}{2}} \rho_n}{\tau_p^{\frac{1}{2}}} \right) \qquad \dots (4.10)$$

where $\tau_n$ and $\tau_p$ are the *minority* carrier lifetimes on the $P$ and $N$ sides respectively. It has already been explained that counter technology usually requires that the carrier lifetime (and therefore the diffusion length) should be long. This requirement is, therefore, consistent with the need to keep $I_s$ low. Equation (4.10) brings out clearly the necessity for having a material of low intrinsic conductivity, so that the quantity $n_i^2$ will be small. Silicon is satisfactory in this respect at ordinary temperatures but germanium, having lower $E_G$, requires to be cooled well below ambient temperatures, otherwise the reverse current is high and the noise level is unacceptable for most purposes.

Equation (4.10) shows the interesting paradox that when the material on either or both sides of the junction has high resistivity, $I_s$ will be relatively large. This is the direct consequence of the fact that the minority carrier concentration is higher in lightly doped crystal (see Chapter 1.6).

In detectors, one side of the junction is extremely shallow and it is assumed that no appreciable drift current can originate therein. On this basis one of the terms in eqn. (4.10) can be omitted. In practical units[6], for a $P$–$N$ junction in silicon, the approximate drift current density is

$$I_s = 1 \cdot 7 \times 10^{-2} \ \rho_p / \frac{1}{n} \quad \mathrm{m\mu A/cm^2} \qquad \dots (4.10a)$$

where $\rho$ is in $\Omega$ cm and $\tau$ is in $\mu$sec. Since a high resistivity is essential for the production of a deep barrier, the consequent increase in $I_s$ must be accepted. It should be noted that $I_s$ is independent of applied bias, up to the breakdown limit. The drift current is not a very troublesome component of reverse current, being, in general, very much less than either of the other two components. It is described at some length here only because it may become relatively more important in future, if other materials are used which have, for example, an exceptionally high carrier mobility and high minority carrier lifetime.

The generation current (b) also has two components, arising from carrier generation in the depletion zones on the two sides of the junction. Each component, however, involves both holes and electrons in equal numbers. As in the case of drift current, the component from the thin surface layer of a detector is thought to be negligible. For a P–N counter the theoretical relationship for generation current, per unit area, is

$$I'_G = n_i q \sqrt{\left(\frac{\epsilon \mu_p}{2\pi}\right)} \cdot \frac{(\rho V)^{\frac{1}{2}}}{\tau_n} \quad \text{e.s.u.} \qquad \dots (4.11)$$

where $\mu_p$ and $\tau_n$ are the hole mobility and electron lifetime of the P material. There is, of course, a similar relationship for an N–P counter. The generation current naturally increases as the volume of the depletion layer increases, and therefore has the same half-power dependance on $\mu$, $\rho$ and $V$ as the barrier depth [see eqn. (4.1b), Chapter 4.5]. The appearance of the minority carrier lifetime in the above relationship is explained in Appendix C. Equation (4.11) shows that this component of reverse current can also be kept low by using material of low intrinsic conductivity and high carrier lifetime.

In practical units[6], if $V$ is in volts, $\rho$ in $\Omega$ cm and $\tau$ in microseconds, the generation current density in a silicon P–N junction is approximately

$$I'_G = 38 \frac{(\rho V)^{\frac{1}{2}}}{\tau_n} \quad \text{m} \mu \text{A cm}^2 \qquad \dots (4.11a)$$

In general (see Appendix C) the carrier generation current in a junction counter exceeds the drift current by about an order of magnitude or more. It has been pointed out by Dearnaley and Whitehead[11], and by others, that the heat treatment necessary for diffusion at the surface has the effect of introducing crystal flaws which reduce the carrier lifetimes and increase the reverse current. If the surface over-compensation could be done at a low temperature the original lifetimes would be better preserved. Minority carrier lifetimes in finished detectors usually appear to be of the order $10^{-5}$ or $10^{-4}$ sec.

Equations (4.10) and (4.11) explain why the physics of a junction counter differs profoundly from that of a junction diode (see Chapter

73

3.2). In the design of the latter, a large depletion zone is unnecessary and undesirable, because of its effect on $I_G$. Consequently, diodes operate well with material of low resistivity and low carrier mobilities. As already mentioned, $I_G'$ is negligible in diodes.

The third component of reverse current, due to surface leakage, is mathematically intractable and a troublesome practical problem. For ordinary detector geometries at a bias of about 100 V it appears, even with good surface conditions, to be larger by up to an order of magnitude than the generation current, and contributes both shot and flicker noise (see Chapter 2.9). Atmospheric contamination occurs very easily and may lead to a catastrophic increase in surface leakage, resulting in breakdown at relatively low bias. Even under the best conditions, breakdown appears to be initiated in the surface rather than in the bulk of the crystal. In a practical experiment it is difficult to distinguish reverse current due to surface leakage from the carrier generation current through the bulk of the crystal. This is because the former often follows an approximately ohmic law (at least for moderate bias) which results in a very rough half-power dependence on applied bias.

In the previous paragraph it was stated that the surface current 'appears' to be much greater than the generation current. This vague wording was used because there is still some doubt on the subject, arising from the difficulty of measuring either current separately and from lack of knowledge of the true carrier generation rate in the depletion zone. If a barrier layer detector is made using a crystal of bulk carrier lifetime in the region of 1 msec, it is invariably found that the total reverse current is greater, by a factor up to 100, than would be expected from eqn. (4.11). The possible explanations for this are as follows.

(a) The surface leakage may be by far the most dominant component of the reverse current.

(b) The bulk carrier lifetime may have been reduced in the processing of the crystal.

(c) Due to surface effects (see Chapter 1.12), the effective carrier lifetime in the detector may be much below the bulk lifetime.

(d) The conclusions of Sah et al.[12], leading to eqn. (4.11) may not be valid, and the true generation rate may be greater than they predict on the basis of the bulk lifetime.

(e) It may not be valid to neglect the contribution to generation current due to the thin surface layer; although this layer is very shallow, it is a region with very low carrier lifetime.

Experiments reported by Hansen and Goulding[13, 14] have done much to clear up the problem. They made guard-ring detectors (described in the next section) of a form which, on theoretical grounds, should eliminate the surface current, and their measurements support the view that they were successful in this respect. The measured bulk lifetime in their $P$-type silicon was in the region of 1 to 1·5 msec. In the finished detector the 'effective lifetime', calculated by eqn. (4.11) from the measured bulk reverse current, was in the region of 300–800 μsec. (There were considerable differences between one crystal and another.) It is, therefore, concluded that high surface current is the main explanation of the relatively large reverse currents obtained in practice. But these experiments also show that one or more of the other possibilities can play some part, increasing the reverse current by a factor of two or three in these detectors.

Before leaving the subject of reverse current it should be mentioned that all the theory described above assumes that the barrier layer does not extend right through the crystal. If this condition is not met, as may be the case in a thin crystal, the back surface and the back contact form one boundary of the barrier layer. The reverse current then depends very much on surface effects and a theoretical treatment of the problem is impracticable. The results are variable, depending on the crystal and the detailed physics of the contact, but in all cases there is a sharp reduction in the effective carrier lifetime and a substantial increase (by about an order of magnitude) in the reverse current. The electrical noise resulting from this leads to inferior energy resolution but counters will operate under these conditions and have uses which are described in Chapter 6, sections 5 and 7.

## 4.9  SURFACE PROTECTION

A number of different approaches have been made to the problem of reducing a counter's sensitivity to the ambient atmosphere. The obvious approach is to mould the body of the crystal in one or other of the many 'potting' materials now available, but these tend to have their own surface effects. For example, epoxy resins applied to $P$-type silicon cause an inversion layer. This difficulty can be partly overcome by the addition of a trace of iodine to the resin and it seems probable that in the near future satisfactory methods of moulding will be found. A coating of Apiezon wax on the sides of the crystal has been tried[15] and found to be very effective in atmospheres which are not excessively moist. Both these approaches have the drawback that they involve hydrogenous materials and, in some applications, lead to spurious signals, due to protons being ejected from them by other particles.

Another approach for *P*-type silicon, which avoids the use of hydrogenous materials, is the deliberate formation of an oxide layer about 0·6 $\mu$ thick. A window is made in this coating by etching through it in order to give access to the basic crystal, and the junction is then formed on the new surface exposed[15]. A similar type of coating using arsenic glass has also been tried.

Enclosure of the crystal in a metal container, which makes no contact with the side faces (see *Figure 4.5*) is also a hopeful approach

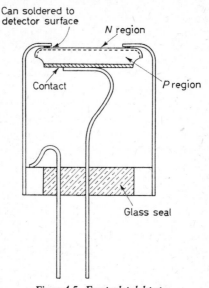

Figure 4.5. Encapsulated detector
(R. L. Williams, *Semiconductor Nuclear Particle Detectors*, Nat. Acad. Sci. (Washington), Publ. 871, p. 28)

but there are difficulties in making an effective seal round the periphery of the sensitive surface without modifying the properties of the junction[16]. It is usual, in 'canning' a crystal, to fill with dry air or nitrogen.

Many experimenters at present prefer to use the crystal without protection and to operate under vacuum. This is stated[9] to give the best results.

None of the above expedients will eliminate the surface leakage current; they serve only to prevent the very large surface leakage which arises from contamination. Hansen and Goulding[13] describe the detector configuration illustrated in *Figure 4.6* whose purpose is to eliminate the effects of surface conductivity. The function of the guard ring is self explanatory. In setting up the counter for operation it is necessary, after adjusting the bias, to set the potentiometer with care so as to make the potential of the guard ring exactly equal to that of the anode. This, of course, requires the use of a bridge or valve voltmeter which does not itself take current.

The primary object in making this detector was to enable accurate measurements to be made of the bulk reverse current for comparison with theory, and also to measure the noise level due to the bulk current

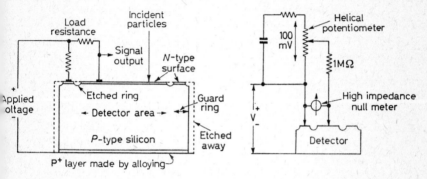

*Figure 4.6. Guard ring detector and Test circuit for leakage current measurements*
(W. Hansen and F. S. Goulding [18])

only. The experiment was successful in this respect. When operated as a counter, however, this configuration was not so successful as had been hoped. Despite the low noise level, resolution with $\alpha$-particles of 5 MeV was 22 keV (f.w.h.m.) which is not up to the best results obtained from counters without guard rings. Hansen and Goulding also observed some double peaking, the cause of which is not yet known.

## 4.10 MATERIALS OTHER THAN *P*-TYPE SILICON

Amsel *et al.*[17] used detectors made from *N*-type silicon of 30–120 $\Omega$ cm, which is equivalent in terms of barrier depth to *P*-type silicon of 90–360 $\Omega$cm approximately. The surface *P* layer was made by diffusion of gallium. They report a reverse current of 0·05 $\mu$A at 30 V bias and breakdown at about 100 V. Resolution was 40 keV for alphas and 30 keV for protons and deuterons. From Blankenship's nomograph (reproduced in Appendix A) such a detector in 100 $\Omega$ silicon at 30 V bias would have a barrier depth of about 30 $\mu$ and would give linearity up to about 6 MeV for $\alpha$-particles. These counters were reported[18] to be more resistant to atmospheric effects and very stable.

$N–P$ junction counters in silicon have not been much used, mainly because, if a counter is to be made from $N$-type material, it is easier and is thought to be more satisfactory to make a surface barrier detector. $N$-type silicon and germanium are only obtainable at present by overcompensation of $P$-type, and this is something of a drawback.

In 4.7 the point was made that the collecting time for a $P–N$ counter is approximately independent of the applied bias and particle penetration. This is a consequence of the fact that some of the slowest carriers must traverse the full barrier depth. In an $N–P$ junction counter this does not apply and collecting time will vary with bias and according to the depth of particle penetration. It will, however, always be somewhat less than in a $P–N$ counter under similar conditions.

Comparatively little attention has been paid to junction counters in germanium and it is clear that the window problem has not been very satisfactorily solved for this material. The necessity for operating at low temperatures makes them unattractive for most purposes, but they are mentioned by Alferov and Koch [19, 20]. Some advantages possessed by germanium are mentioned in Chapter 5.5, in connexion with surface barrier counters.

Semiconductors other than silicon and germanium are not yet available in sufficiently perfect crystals to meet the lifetime requirements for high resolution detectors, but it is to be hoped that this problem will soon be overcome. In searching for better materials the main object is to find a crystal which will have an energy gap at least as great as that of silicon (to permit operation at ambient temperatures) but which will have a substantially greater atomic number. Particle penetration would then be reduced, so that a wider energy spectrum could be covered with a given barrier depth. Unfortunately, there is a tendency for the energy gap to decrease with increasing atomic number and few materials seem likely to meet the requirement.

As in the case of the bulk detector, gallium arsenide ($E_G = 1\cdot35$, $Z = 32$) appears hopeful, but the carrier lifetime (about $10^{-8}$ sec) is not high enough to give good resolution. Rediker[21] reports successful $P–N$ diodes in gallium arsenide, made by diffusion with zinc to form the $N$ layer. These performed satisfactorily as low reverse-current diodes and as variable capacitors. The low lifetime is beneficial in such applications, since it gives high-speed switching and good h.f. response. Another possibly hopeful material is bismuth sulphide ($Bi_2S_3$, $Z = 43$) but very little is known about its properties as yet. The energy gap is reported[22] to exceed 1 eV.

Organic semiconductors have also received some consideration. There are a great many organic compounds which show semiconducting properties and only very few have yet been investigated. Chynoweth† gives a brief account of results so far and these are most discouraging. The crystals show very heavy trapping, lifetimes appear to be of the order of nanoseconds and mobilities are in the region of $1 \ cm^2/Vsec.$

REFERENCES

[1] McKAY, K. G., *Phys. Rev.* 76 (1949) 1537
[2] DONOVAN, P. F., *Semiconductor Nuclear Particle Detectors*, Nat. Acad. Sci. (Washington), Publ. 871, App. B
[3] BLANKENSHIP, L. J., *Semiconductor Nuclear Particle Detectors*, Nat. Acad. Sci. (Washington), Publ. 871, p. 43
[4] MILLER, G. L., and GIBSON, W. M., *Proceedings of a Conference on Nuclear Electronics* (May 1961), I.A.E.A.
[5] FRIEDLAND, S. S., MAYER, J. W. and WIGGINS, J. S., *Nucleonics* 18, (1960) 2, p. 54
[6] McKENZIE, J. M. and WAUGH, J. B. S., *Proceedings of Seventh Scintillation Counter Symposium*, Inst. Radio Engrs, N.Y., N.S.7, Nos. 2 and 3 (Sept. 1960)
[7] BLANKENSHIP, J. L. and BORKOWSKI, C. J., *ibid.* p. 190
[8] *Semiconductor Detectors*, Nucleonics 18, 5 (1960) p. 98
[9] JACKSON, R. S., WEBB, P. P. and WILLIAMS, R. L., *Solid State Radiation Detectors*, Inst. Radio Engrs, N.Y., N.S.8, No. 1 (Jan. 1961) p. 29
[10] MILLER, G. L., BROWN, W. L., DONOVAN, P. F. and MACKINTOSH, J. M., *Proceedings of Seventh Scintillation Counter Symposium*, Inst. Radio Engrs, N.Y., N.S.7, Nos. 2 and 3 (Sept. 1960) p. 185
[11] DEARNALEY, G. and WHITEHEAD, A. B., *A.E.R.E. Rep.* R-3662 (1961)
[12] SAH, C. J., NOYCE, R. N. and SHOCKLEY, W., *Proc. Inst. Radio Engrs,* N.Y., 45 (1957) 1228
[13] HANSEN, W. and GOULDING, F. S., *Semiconductor Nuclear Particle Detectors*, Nat. Acad. Sci. (Washington), Publ. 871, p. 202
[14] HANSEN, W. and GOULDING, F. S., *Proceedings of a Conference on Nuclear Electronics* (May, 1961), I.A.E.A.
[15] GIBSON, W. M., *Semiconductor Nuclear Particle Detectors*, Nat. Acad. Sci. (Washington), Publ. 871, p. 232
[16] WILLIAMS, R. L., *ibid.* p. 28
[17] AMSEL, G., BARUCH, P. and SMULKOVSKI, O., *Solid State Radiation Detectors*, Inst. Radio Engrs, N.Y., N.S.8, No. 1 (Jan. 1961) p. 21
[18] AMSEL, G., *Semiconductor Nuclear Particle Detectors*, Nat. Acad. Sci. (Washington), Publ. 871, p. 35
[19] ALFEROV, B. M. *et al., J. tech. Phys., Moscow* 25 (1955) 11
[20] KOCH, L., MESSIER, J. and VALIN, J., *Solid State Radiation Detectors*, Inst. Radio Engrs, N.Y., N.S.8, No. 1 (Jan. 1961) p. 43
[21] REDIKER, R. H., *Semiconductor Nuclear Particle Detectors*, Nat. Acad. Sci. (Washington), Publ. 871, p. 164
[22] SCANLON, W. W., *ibid.* p. 145

† Discussion following Ref. 22.

# 5

# BARRIER LAYER DETECTORS:
# SURFACE BARRIER TYPE

## 5.1  INTRODUCTION

DETECTORS of this type are identical in principle and very similar in
their properties to the junction detectors already described. Most of
them are made from silicon and they have a depletion zone very close
to the sensitive surface; the difference lies in the method of obtaining
a surface junction. Early work on the development is described by
Walter *et al.*[1] and much subsequent work has been reported by
Blankenship [2-6], by Dearnaley and Whitehead [7-9], and others.

## 5.2  DESCRIPTION

$N$-type silicon (or germanium), when exposed to the atmosphere,
develops an inversion layer on the surface, due to oxidation. The
inversion layer is very thin and therefore a junction exists close enough
to the surface to meet the requirements for a counter; it fails only
because the surface layer is not sufficiently conducting to provide an
electrode. To make a counter this surface is given a thin metallic
coating; gold is usually employed, but nickel or other metals can be
used. *Figure 5.1* illustrates a typical surface barrier detector and is for
comparison with *Figure 4.1(a)*. The dimensions are similar to those of
a junction detector and the electrode connexions are similar, except
that the polarity is reversed to maintain the reversed bias condition
across the junction (the $N$ side must be positive). The impedance
diagram is not drawn because it is identical with that of *Figure 4.1(b)*.

The formation of a barrier (Schottky barrier) when a metal contact
is applied to a semiconductor has long been known and is the basis of
the copper oxide rectifier, the selenium rectifier and the 'cat's
whisker' crystal rectifiers used as signal detectors in early radio
receiving sets. The photo-electric properties have been exploited in
various types of 'barrier-layer' photocells. The detailed physics is
very complicated and, perhaps, not yet fully understood. A simplified account is given by Cusack[10, pp. 248-254], which includes a mathematical treatment similar to that of Chapter 4 and Appendix C. The

results are identical to those for a diffused junction and the same equations apply to the thickness of the depletion zone, the capacitance and the reverse current. Suitable modifications must, of course, be

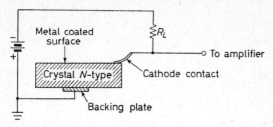

*Figure 5.1*

made for the fact that the junctions are *N–P*; for example, the depletion layer depth,

$$X = \left( \frac{\epsilon V}{2\pi q N} \right)^{\frac{1}{2}} \qquad \ldots (5.1)$$

where $N$ is the concentration of donors in the bulk of the crystal.

Except for the reversal in polarity, the electric field and the potential in the depletion zone follow the same laws, and the mathematical treatment is similar to that of Chapter 4.5. The nomographs of Appendix A apply to junction and to surface barrier detectors. In a surface barrier counter the junction might be expected, from the

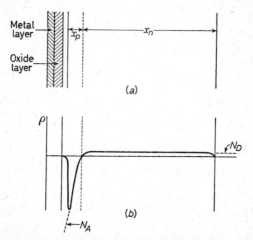

*Figure 5.2. Depletion zone and space charge distribution*

physics of its formation, to be always abrupt and this is borne out in practice. Dearnaley and Whitehead[8] find the capacitance to follow very closely a law of proportionality to $V^{-\frac{1}{2}}$.

It is not easy to draw a diagram of the space charge distribution, similar to *Figure 4.2*, because the distribution of acceptor centres near the surface is unknown. However, it appears certain[11] that some of these centres lie below the oxide layer and it may, therefore, be inferred that the junction is not at the oxide layer but a few crystal lattices away from it. It also seems probable that the metal coating will diffuse a little into the oxide and neutralize the external surface states (slow states). *Figure 5.2* has been drawn on these assumptions.

## 5.3 METHOD OF PREPARATION

The method described here of making a surface barrier detector is that adopted by Dearnaley and Whitehead and is described in greater detail in[9].

### Preparation of a Surface Barrier Detector in Silicon

The $N$-type material is cut to a suitable size and shape and is ground and lapped on all faces. It is good practice to clean the crystal before etching by boiling for a few minutes in concentrated nitric acid. The etching is done with C.P.4A, which consists of:

|  |  |
|---|---|
| concentrated nitric acid . . . | 2 vol. |
| glacial acetic acid . . . . | 1 vol. |
| 40 per cent hydrofluoric acid . . | 1 vol. |

This takes 5–10 min in a bath cooled to 0 °C, and the etch is then diluted with demineralized water and the crystal washed and dried on filter paper.

Gold is normally used for the surface coating since it is chemically stable, highly conducting and charged particle emission is inhibited by the high atomic number. A mica mask having a keyhole shape (see *Figure 5.3*)† is clamped to the surface and gold is deposited by vaporization *in vacuo* to a thickness of 50–100 µg/cm². For a fission fragment detector, to avoid a 'window' problem, this should be kept near to the lower limit.

A new mask is now fixed which covers all the circular area of the keyhole shape and further gold is evaporated on to the contact area to a thickness of about 500 µg/cm². The crystal is then placed on clean

---

† *Figure 5.3* and the description of the mounting plate have been rendered obsolete by the adoption of an evaporated film of aluminium for the back contact (see Chapter 10.2 and also Dearnaley[12]).

filter paper in a covered box for 2–3 days to allow full development of the surface oxide, which appears to take place through the gold.

The mounting plate material recommended is Kovar, which has the same coefficient of thermal expansion as silicon, and a stud is provided (see *Figure 5.3*) to avoid having the mounting paste squeezed out to the edges of the crystal where it would contaminate the side faces. F.S.P. 36 flake silver paste (Johnson, Matthey & Co., London) is used to attach the crystal to the mounting plate.

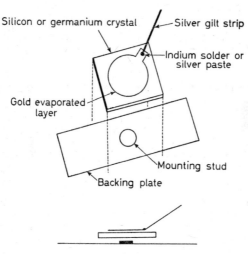

*Figure 5.3*

(G. Dearnaley and A. B. Whitehead[9])

The front contact is made by a short length of silver-gold alloy strip and is fixed with F.S.P. 36. It is very important that the paste should not flow on to the silicon. F.S.P. 36 is best hardened by gentle heating at 50° C for about 10 h.

The suggestion is made that a more nearly ohmic back contact, and a stronger one, may be obtained by leaving the back surface in a lapped condition, or by treating it after etching with a fine abrasive.

Dearnaley and Whitehead, making counters by this method, report a success rate of 80 per cent. This is for the 'naked' counter used *in vacuo* without 'canning' or encapsulation. The use of a keyhole-shaped mask is, of course, not obligatory and a rectangular shape is more suitable for many purposes.

Dearnaley and Whitehead further describe the modifications to the above for making a germanium counter: (*a*) the etch is used at room

7                                        83

temperature because the reaction is slower, and (*b*) the backing plate and front connexion are secured with indium solder, this being more resistant to low temperature cycling.

In using the detectors a mask or collimator is fitted to restrict the aperture to the area of the thin gold coating. There are 'canning' problems with surface barrier detectors also, since it is difficult to attach anything to the periphery of the gold coating without damaging the surface and, in any case, the adhesion of the gold is not very strong. An interesting method of overcoming this problem, by mounting in a ceramic ring prior to gold coating, is described by Fox[13]. Encapsulation in epoxy resins is also used[14] but this is stated to have adverse effects on the surface leakage current and on the success rate[7].

## 5.4   CHARACTERISTICS IN COMPARISON WITH JUNCTION DETECTORS

In highly refined silicon the residual impurity is boron, an acceptor. Consequently, $N$-type silicon owes its properties to over-compensation and the minority carrier lifetime is therefore reduced. However, crystals with a carrier lifetime in the millisecond region can be obtained and this is perfectly adequate. Moreover, the process of making a surface barrier counter does not involve heat treatment of any significance and the carrier lifetime of the original crystal is therefore better preserved. It is claimed[8, 2] that surface barrier counters have significantly longer carrier lifetimes, and consequently lower, bulk reverse current, than junction counters. This is, of course, advantageous in reducing noise and improving energy resolution.

As indicated in *Figure 5.3*, the gold-covered sensitive surface is usually confined to a central part of the counter face, thus giving a longer and more resistive path for the surface leakage current. On the other hand, current is now able to by-pass the barrier layer through the bulk material at the edge of the gold coating and there is, in effect, a 'bulk leakage current'. There is little apparent difference in the behaviour of the counter as a result of this feature and no distinction is made in this study between the two types of leakage current.

Since the electron mobility in silicon is about three times that of the holes, $N$-type crystal tends to have much lower resistivity than $P$-type. However, the barrier depth depends on the effective concentration of impurity centres [see eqn. (5.1)] and the availability of suitable crystal appears to be much the same for $N$- as for $P$-type[8]. The limitations imposed by barrier depth (see Chapter 4.4) are therefore much the same for silicon surface barrier detectors as for silicon junction detectors.

The window problem is much the same in surface barrier counters as in junction counters; it is significant, in a good detector, only for fission fragments. A thin, homogeneous surface layer is, however, much easier to obtain on a surface barrier counter.

$N$-type silicon is rather less sensitive to atmospheric contamination than $P$-type[15] and therefore protection of the side surfaces is not so important. On the other hand, the sensitive surface appears[2] to be rather more vulnerable than that of a junction counter, the contaminants being able to penetrate the thin gold layer with little difficulty. Subject to their being carefully protected from contamination, surface barrier counters are very stable; Dearnaley and Whitehead, for example, report the use of detectors for periods of 15 months without deterioration[8].

It was pointed out in Chapter 4.7 that in $P–N$ junction detectors, where at least a few of the holes make the full transit of the depletion zone, the collecting time is approximately constant, being independent of bias volts and particle penetration. This does not apply to surface barrier counters, which have $N–P$ junctions. For particles which penetrate only a fraction of the barrier depth the collecting time is less than for a $P$-type counter under similar conditions and varies according to penetration. Since, however, collecting time for both types is less than the rise time of the amplifier, this fact has little significance in relation to time resolution.

## 5.5   GERMANIUM SURFACE BARRIER DETECTORS

The first detailed report on germanium surface barrier detectors is by Walter *et al.*[1] of the Oak Ridge National Laboratory. Their report describes the theory of operation and the method of making the counters in great detail. Both surfaces were coated with gold by vaporization *in vacuo*; the back contact so produced is, of course, non-ohmic, but as it operates under forward bias this does not have a serious effect on the counter performance. Contact to both surfaces was made by indium pressure pads. The counters were used for detection of $\alpha$-particles and fission fragments from spin oriented nuclei at low temperatures, so the necessity for cooling the detectors was, if anything, an advantage.

Bilaniuk and co-workers have described in two reports [16, 17] the use of a multiple counter array in the focal plane of a magnetic analyser. The barrier depths were in the region of 50 $\mu$ and for particles having a range, in germanium, up to this limit, simultaneous resolution was obtained in momentum and in energy. They state that germanium was selected for the purpose because of the superior time stability, as compared with gold–silicon counters, and they report a signal-to-noise ratio of 100:1. These counters did operate at room temperature but the noise level was greater by an order of magnitude.

Pantchechnikev[18] developed a method of making germanium counters encapsulated in synthetic resin, and McKenzie and Bromley[19] also report on the use of this technique. Most of the general information given here on the characteristics of these detectors comes from the reports by Dearnaley and Whitehead[7,8], who use them unprotected, *in vacuo*.

The concentration of carriers in extrinsic germanium remains approximately constant over a wide range of temperature, showing a fall of only a few per cent between 270 and 70° K. The nomograph in Appendix A therefore gives reasonably accurate depletion zone depths for most conditions of operation. The higher atomic number of germanium gives it about twice the stopping power of silicon; also, it is more easily refined and can be obtained with lower concentrations of impurity centres. Linearity of pulse height with particle energy can, therefore, be obtained with a lower bias than with a comparable silicon counter. On the other hand, breakdown tends to occur at a lower bias level (50–200 V) with germanium and the energy spectrum which can be covered remains much the same as that for silicon (see Chapter 4.4).

The surface conductivity of germanium is higher than that of silicon and remains so even at low temperatures. The use of a stud on the backing plate, making contact over a small central area only, helps to reduce the reverse current by making the surface leakage path as long as possible. The greater surface conductivity may explain the fact that reverse current is somewhat more variable than with silicon, since the condition of the surface can affect its conductivity by several orders of magnitude.

The carrier mobilities in germanium at 77° K are of the order $10^4$ cm²/V sec. This gives a theoretical reduction of collecting time by about an order of magnitude, to $5 \times 10^{-10}$ sec. It is impossible at present to check this by experiment but it seems unlikely that such rapid collection can really be obtained. In relation to time intervals of this order, ambipolar effects (see Chapter 2.4) are likely to be very significant and the time constant of the crystal base (resistance and capacitance of the bulk crystal, outside the depletion zone) will also be significant. It has been verified by Orman, using a sampling oscilloscope, that a rise time of less than 3 nsec was obtained in one particular experiment with 5 MeV α-particles[8]. In another case, where the calculated rise time was 1 nsec, the experimental results showed it to be not greater than 20 nsec[1].

Dearnaley and Whitehead[8] tabulate the known $n,p$ reactions of germanium, and conclude that it should give a lower response to fast neutrons than silicon. They have verified, qualitatively, that a germanium counter gives a lower count from a flux of fast neutrons than a silicon counter having the same barrier depth, and they point out that a further advantage will be gained from the fact that germanium stops a proton of given energy with three times fewer nuclei/cm² than silicon. Germanium counters, therefore, would be superior to those made from silicon for operating in a background flux of neutrons.

Germanium counters, at 77° K, give very much the same energy resolution as those made from silicon at ambient temperature.

## REFERENCES

[1] WALTER, F. J., DABBS, J. W. T., ROBERTS, L. D., and WRIGHT, H. W., *O.R.N.L. Rep.* CF58-11-99 (1958)

[2] BLANKENSHIP, J. L., *Semiconductor Nuclear Particle Detectors*, Nat. Acad. Sci. (Washington), Publ. 871, p. 43

[3] BLANKENSHIP, J. L. and BORKOWSKI, C. J., *Solid State Radiation Detectors*, Inst. Radio Engrs, N.Y., N.S.8, No. 1 (Jan. 1961) p. 17

[4] BLANKENSHIP, J. L. and BORKOWSKI, C. J., *Proceedings of a Conference on Nuclear Electronics* (May 1961), I.A.E.A.

[5] BLANKENSHIP, J. L. and BORKOWSKI, C. J., *Proceedings of the Seventh Scintillation Counter Symposium*, Inst. Radio Engrs, N.Y., N.S.7, Nos. 2 and 3 (Sept. 1960) p. 190

[6] BLANKENSHIP, J. L. and BORKOWSKI, C. J., *Bull. Amer. phys. Soc.* 5, No. 1 (1960)

[7] DEARNALEY, G. and WHITEHEAD, A. B., *A.E.R.E. Rep.* R-3437 (1960)

[8] DEARNALEY, G. and WHITEHEAD, A. B., *A.E.R.E. Rep.* R-3662 (1961)

[9] DEARNALEY, G. and WHITEHEAD, A. B., *Nucleonics* 19, No. 1 (1961) p. 72

[10] CUSACK, N., *Electrical and Magnetic Properties of Solids*, Longmans, London

[11] STATZ, H., *Semiconductor Nuclear Particle Detectors*, Nat. Acad. Sci. (Washington), Publ. 871, p. 99

[12] DEARNALEY, G., *A.E.R.E. Rep.* R-3874 (1961)

[13] FOX, R. J., *Semiconductor Nuclear Particle Detectors*, Nat. Acad. Sci. (Washington), Publ. 871, App. B.

[14] McKENZIE, J. M. and WAUGH, J. B. S., *Proceedings of Seventh Scintillation Counter Symposium*, Inst. Radio Engrs, N.Y., N.S.7, Nos. 2 and 3 (Sept. 1960)

[15] AMSEL, G., *Semiconductor Nuclear Particle Detectors*, Nat. Acad. Sci. (Washington), Publ. 871, p. 35

[16] BILANIUK, O. M., HAMAN, A. K. and MARSH, B. B., *University of Rochester Rep.* AT(30–1)-875 (1960)

[17] BILANIUK, O. M. and MARSH, B. B., *Proceedings of a Conference on Nuclear Electronics* (May 1961), I.A.E.A.

[18] PANTCHECHNIKOFF, J. I., *Rev. sci. Instrum.* 23 (1952) 135

[19] McKENZIE, J. M. and BROMLEY, D. A., *Phys. Rev. Letters* 2 (1959) 303

# 6

# BARRIER LAYER DETECTORS: GENERAL

## 6.1 Introduction

THE applications of diffused junction detectors and surface barrier detectors in nuclear physics are largely identical, the two types being interchangeable in nearly all cases. The results obtained (and their characteristics) are also very similar. The behaviour and performance of the two types are, therefore, discussed together here.

## 6.2 Electrical Noise and Interference Effects

The description of the noise problem in bulk detectors (Chapter 2.9) applies equally to barrier layer detectors and will not be repeated here. There is, however, a difference in the importance of noise in the two cases. Whereas, in bulk detectors, the main limitation on energy resolution is the homogeneity problem, this is not the case in barrier layer counters, which can give a resolution closely approaching the theoretical limit imposed by statistical variations in the number of carriers created. Consequently, further improvement in resolution is to be achieved only by further work on the noise problem. As far as the detector itself is concerned this is mainly a matter of reducing the surface leakage current, or eliminating its effects by some such expedient as the guard-ring configuration. Both these aspects of the problem have already been described and there is nothing to add here.

The amplifying system is itself a source of electrical noise and, broadly speaking, contributes about the same amount as the detector. When all reasonable steps have been taken to reduce both these sources of noise to a minimum it is advantageous to consider the system as a whole with a view to optimizing the parameters involved. This has been done by Hansen and Goulding, whose results are briefly described in the chapter on electronics later in this study (see Chapter 9.4).

Particle detectors usually operate in the vicinity of an accelerator and it is found that semiconductor counters, with their high gain amplifying systems, are very subject to electrical interference. In most cases this problem can be overcome by good screening and sound design, but care is needed. Barrier layer counters are very resistant to magnetic effects, which is a valuable characteristic in relation to their possible applications in conjunction with a magnetic spectrometer. An appreciable effect in a silicon barrier layer counter would not be expected below about 50,000 G[1].

## 6.3 ENERGY RESOLUTION

Particle spectrometry by pulse height analysis is described in Appendix D, where methods of defining energy resolution are briefly explained. The first requirement for good energy resolution is, ideally, complete collection. This requires that the sensitive depth be greater than the range of the particle, that the carrier lifetime be long enough, and that the clipping time constant be long compared with the collecting time (Chapter 9.2). There is a further requirement, that the detector bias be high enough for efficient collection; resolution is not usually good with a bias less than about 5 V even if the other requirements are, apparently, satisfied. These factors are discussed in more detail elsewhere in this study but it is necessary to point out that, to some extent, compromise is needed to obtain the best results at a given point in the energy spectrum.

The effect of variation of bias on resolution is illustrated in *Figure 6.1*, reproduced from the paper by Friedland *et al.*[2] At zero bias the sensitive depth is less than the penetration of the particles. At 6 V the barrier is nearly deep enough to stop the lower energy particles but collection is less than 100 per cent and resolution is still poor. The optimum for the lower energy particles is at about 16 V, but 22 V appears better for the higher energies. With a further increase in bias volts rapid deterioration sets in as the noise level increases.

The behaviour described above is not typical, it being possible with many good detector/amplifier systems to obtain good resolution over a much wider band of bias setting and energy, but it serves to illustrate the point made by Amsel *et al.*[3] that change of bias alone does not give adequate control. They state that a study of the reaction $^{16}O(d, \alpha)^{14}N$ is impossible with 2,000 $\Omega$ silicon but easy with a detector made from 35 $\Omega$ silicon. In fact, it would seem to be necessary, for maximum resolution over a wide energy band, to have several detectors with different parent resistivities.

Another basic requirement for good resolution is crystal homogeneity. Carrier lifetime can vary by several orders of magnitude in different parts of the same crystal and there are sometimes small centres (at crystal defects) where lifetime is extremely short. For full collection the lifetime in all parts of the barrier zone must be large compared with the collecting time.

Given a homogeneous crystal and good carrier collection, energy resolution is limited by noise (in the counter and in the amplifier) and by statistical variations in the number of carriers released by a particle of given energy. The statistics problem is common to all forms of detector and its effect on resolution is fundamental to the system concerned. It is usual to estimate on the assumption that the number

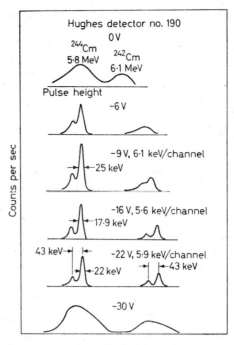

*Figure 6.1. Pulse height distribution of* $^{242}$Cm *and* $^{244}$Cm
*as a function of applied bias*

(H. Mann, Argonne Nat. Lab.[3])

of carriers released will vary according to a Poisson distribution, and the standard deviation is then,

$$\sigma = \sqrt{N}$$

where $N$ is the average.

In the case of primary ions released by an incident particle in a gaseous counter it has been shown by Fano[4] that $\sigma^2$ is less than $N$ by a factor $F$, which lies between $\frac{1}{3}$ and $\frac{1}{2}$. No Fano factor has been found to apply to the production of carrier pairs in solids and the statistics appear to conform to a Poisson distribution.

Apart from the Fano factor the advantage, as regards statistics, lies with a detection system in which a large number of primary carriers is produced. The ratio of the standard deviation to the mean is a measure of the resolution, and for a Poisson distribution this is clearly equal to $N^{-\frac{1}{2}}$. A large value of $N$ therefore gives good resolution. Despite the effect of the Fano factor the semiconductor detector offers advantages in this respect over the gaseous ion counter. This fact is shown in the following table[5].

TABLE 6.1. RESOLUTION SPREAD DUE TO STATISTICS FOR AN
α-PARTICLE, 5·3 MeV

| In a gas | |
|---|---|
| $\epsilon = 28$ eV/pair<br>$\sigma = 270$ pairs<br>$\sigma = 7\cdot5$ keV<br>Half width $= 2\cdot36\,\sigma$<br>$\qquad = 18$ keV | Fano factor $= F$, where $\frac{1}{3} < F < \frac{1}{2}$ |
| *In silicon* | |
| $\epsilon = 3\cdot5$ eV/pair<br>$\sigma = 1{,}200$ pairs<br>$\sigma = 4\cdot4$ keV<br>Half width $= 10$ keV | Assume $F = 1$ |

The figure 10 keV, given above, is the theoretical limit of resolution for a silicon counter and is equivalent to 0·2 per cent (f.w.h.m.). In practice some further loss of resolution must occur due to noise but under favourable conditions it is possible to obtain a resolution of 0·3 per cent on α-particles of this energy.

The following table reproduces data from Bromley[6] in which a very interesting and detailed comparison is made between semiconductor counters and other detecting devices. The figures relate to experimental results using the devices stated with their associated equipment. Bearing in mind the simplicity of the barrier layer counter and its associated electronics (as compared, for example, with a scintillator plus photomultiplier and stabilized supplies) the advantages in resolution are most impressive.

Barrier layer counters are ideally suited for the detection and energy resolution of α-particles, and these are generally employed to test their performance. From many examples of α-particle spectrometry in the literature two are reproduced in *Figures 6.2* and *6.3*,

TABLE 6.2. COMPARISON OF ENERGY RESOLUTION
OBTAINABLE WITH DIFFERENT SYSTEMS

| System | Per cent |
|---|---|
| Photo emulsions | 5 |
| Scintillation methods | 3–2 |
| Gas counters: | |
|    (*a*) ionization | 1 |
|    (*b*) proportional | 2 |
| Semiconductor barrier layer | |
|    counters | 0·7–0·3 |
| Magnetic spectrometers | 0·5–0·01 |

below. These results are representative of the behaviour of the best counters.

*Figure 6.2* is from Blankenship's paper[7]. The detector was a 25 mm² surface barrier counter in material of resistivity 2,000 $\Omega$ cm. It maintained the same resolution of 15 keV ( = 0·27 per cent on the central

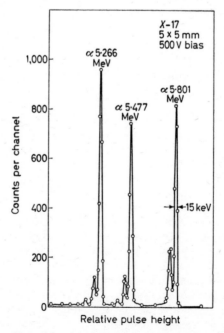

*Figure 6.2. α-particle spectrum with a gold-silicon detector*

(J. L. Blankenship[7])

peak) with bias varied between 50 and 500 V. Blankenship repeated this experiment with the detector cooled to 78° K and obtained a resolution of 13·5 keV, the reverse current being now reduced by two orders of magnitude. This suggests that the various sources of noise are contributing as follows to the 15 keV shown in *Figure 6.2*:

Statistics: 11 keV (by calculation on the basis of a Poisson distribution)
Detector noise: 6·5 keV
Other sources (amplifier noise plus all other factors): 7·8 keV

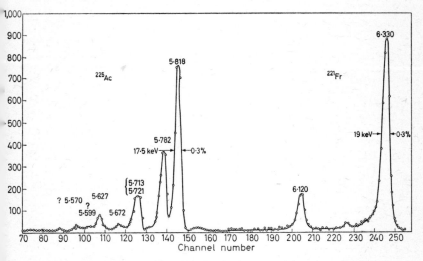

Figure 6.3. *Pulse height distribution of the* $^{229}$Th *daughters α-particle spectrum; bias 16·5 V, approximately 5·0* keV/*channel*

(H. Mann, Argonne Nat. Lab.[2])

*Figure 6.3* is reproduced from Friedland *et al.*[2], and the relevant portion of the text is quoted verbatim: 'The resolution of small area diffused junctions is typically less than 1 per cent for 5 MeV α-particles. *Figure 6.3* illustrates the resolution of a 1 mm² unit to the daughter spectrum of $^{229}$Th, and shows a 0·3 per cent of 18 keV width of the pulse height distribution at half maximum counting rate. It has been found that the width of the pulse-height distribution increases as the area of the units increases'.

The tendency towards inferior resolution in larger detectors is inherent in the design and is due partly to the increased noise level arising from the higher reverse current, partly to the effects of inhomogeneity, and partly to the increased self-capacitance of the device. The dependence of resolution on counter area must be remembered when comparing reported results. However, good results can be obtained with counters up to 1 cm² in area; Blankenship[7] shows 17 keV (f.w.h.m.) with alphas of 5·8 MeV (= 0·3 per cent), but this is most exceptional, and a figure of 0·4 to 0·7 per cent is more usual.

The problem of obtaining good energy resolution depends on several factors other than the properties of the detector and amplifier, e.g. source and target thickness, collimation, scattering, etc. Methods of reducing these effects to a minimum are described in the paper by Amsel et al., already mentioned[3]. One of the biggest problems is a tendency for the detector to be flooded by the elastically scattered particles. Much can be done by using a barrier no deeper than is necessary and a clipping time no longer than necessary (to reduce collection by diffusion). Amsel et al. were able to work through 10⁴ counts/sec of scattered particles.

A study of the various results suggests that, at their best, surface barrier counters are superior in energy resolution to junction detectors. This may be due (as suggested by Dearnaley and Whitehead[1]) to the better preservation of carrier lifetime by avoiding heat treatment in their preparation.

Barrier layer counters are not very sensitive to neutrons or to β- or γ-particles and it is possible to work through appreciable backgrounds of these radiations. In the case of neutrons this facility is limited by deterioration of energy resolution due to progressive radiation damage.

## 6.4   PARTICLE SPECTROMETRY

The main advantage to the nuclear physicist in the employment of barrier layer detectors is the fact that, with the aid of pulse height analysis, it offers a simple method of high resolution particle spectrometry, with strict linearity regardless of the nature of the particle. For particles consisting of only a few nucleons this facility is available only up to very moderate energies at present but a wider range of linearity is obtainable with heavier particles. In this section a few selected results are presented and described.

The first example, *Figure 6.4*, is from a paper by Blankenship and Borkowski[5]. It was obtained with a surface barrier counter of area 6·3 mm² and shows the alpha 0, 60, 103 and 159 lines. The ratios of the areas under the lines are in agreement with magnetic spectrograph data. These lines would not be resolved with a Frisch-grid pulse-ion chamber, which gives resolution not better than 26 keV.

*Figure 6.5*[8], was obtained with a silicon *P–N* junction counter. The two lines 39 keV apart are fully resolved. The straight line on the graph relates the channel number of the analyser with particle energy, as shown on the scale on the right.

*Figure 6.6* shows two spectra of heavy ions obtained by Bromley[6]. They show the effects of bombardment with $^{12}C$ and $^{16}O$ nuclei on

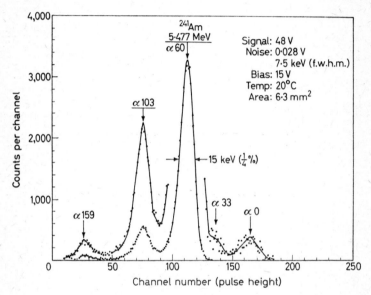

*Figure 6.4*

(J. L. Blankenship and C. J. Borkowski[5], by courtesy of Inst. Radio Engrs, New York)

films of carbon and silicon monoxide, respectively. Bromley states that, 'for the first time, the junctions make possible the unambiguous resolution of the ion groups elastically scattered from different target and contaminant nuclei as well as the inelastically scattered groups'. For heavy ions, barrier layer counters have quite a good range of linearity; to 160 MeV for $^{16}O$, for example.

Amsel and Smulkowski[9] give results of their work with junction detectors and an interesting description of their experimental techniques is given[3]. *Figure 6.7* shows the elastic scattering of deuterons from a target of aluminium oxide at a laboratory angle of 165°. Low energy protons from the reaction $^{12}C(d,p)^{13}C$ are also stopped in the barrier and are well resolved.

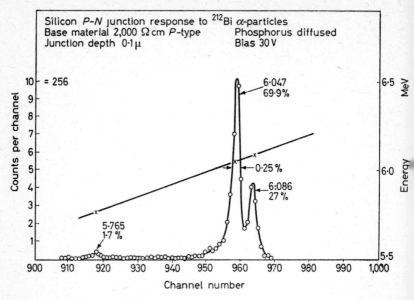

*Figure 6.5*

(J. M. Mckenzie and G. T. Ewan[8], by courtesy of Inst. Radio Engrs, New York)

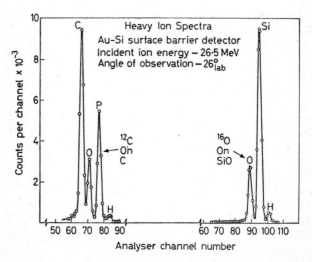

*Figure 6.6*

(D. A. Bromley[6])

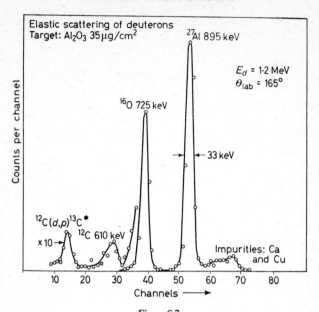

*Figure 6.7*

(G. Amsel, *Semiconductor Nuclear Particle Detectors*, Nat. Acad. Sci. (Washington), Publ. 871, p. 38)

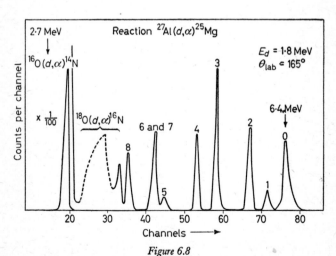

*Figure 6.8*

(G. Amsel, *Semiconductor Nuclear Particle Detectors*, Nat. Acad. Sci, (Washington), Publ. 871, p. 38)

*Figure 6.8*, from the same source, illustrates the results of investigating the reaction $^{27}Al(d, \alpha)^{25}Mg$. The numerous peaks correspond to various excitation levels in $^{25}Mg$.

A typical example of a study of elastic scattering is shown in *Figure 6.9*.[6] The ordinates show the differential cross-section plotted against angle of scatter; the dotted line is the result predicted by classical mechanics and the solid line is the quantum mechanical prediction. The points are experimental results obtained with a barrier layer detector of unspecified type.

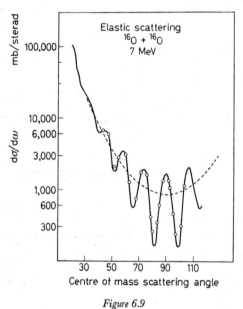

*Figure 6.9*

(D. A. Bromley[6])

In scattering experiments the simplicity of the associated electronics and the smallness of the detectors is an advantage. It is usual to employ a counter having a rectangular aperture, suited to the geometry of the experiment, and an array of counters may be operated close to each other to give simultaneous records. A common amplification and recording system may be used by adopting the method of Bilaniuk[10]. The study of scattering at high angles is particularly facilitated by the small counter size.

Pulse height spectra obtained with barrier layer counters seem always to have a 'low energy tail', which limits the sensitivity of the system for low energy, low intensity components of the radiation. a good example of the 'tail' is seen in *Figure 6.5*, where there is a continuum of signals, at a low count rate, extending over the channels below 950. The cause of this is not understood; Chetham-Strode *et al.*[11] investigated the phenomenon, using silicon surface barrier counters made from crystals of resistivity 150–3,600 $\Omega$cm and minority carrier lifetimes 400–1,500 μsec. They conclude that the tail is *not* due to

(a) scattering,
(b) inhomogeneities in the gold or oxide surface layers,
(c) noise,
(d) pile-up,
(e) back-scattering or source thickness.

They also showed that the fraction of low energy pulses was independent of

(a) bias volts, between 20–400 V,
(b) silicon resistivity from 150–3,600 $\Omega$cm,
(c) temperature, between 246 and 298° K.

Scanning the aperture of the counter with a mask also had no effect on the tail.

## 6.5 d$E$/d$x$ Detectors and Time Resolution

All barrier layer detectors receiving fast charged particles will respond linearly to the energy actually lost in the sensitive volume and for some purposes it is advantageous to design the detector with this specific employment in view. In such applications there is often a requirement to have a thin detector, which will absorb only a little energy, and to make the whole volume sensitive. This can be done with surface barrier techniques, and one method of preparation is described by Fox[12].

In brief, a thin wafer of crystal, typically about 0·2 mm thick, is used and the bias is set deliberately to extend the barrier through to the back contact. This results in increased reverse current, as mentioned in the final paragraph of Chapter 4.8, with a consequent increase in noise and loss of resolution. However, these penalties can be accepted and are reduced to a minimum by employing a crystal of high resistivity. This enables the necessary barrier width to be obtained with low bias and therefore with low surface leakage current. Fox, using 2,000 $\Omega$cm $N$-type silicon obtained nearly windowless performance at both surfaces with bias about 25 V. With an area of 0·5 cm$^2$ the resolution on 5 MeV $\alpha$-particles can be as high as 0·4 per cent (f.w.h.m.). Such detectors are useful in themselves for particle discrimination and are also used for this purpose in conjunction with $E$ detectors, as described in section 7.

With existing systems of amplification there is little object in trying to improve the time resolution of which the detectors themselves are capable, but it is interesting to note that the theory of carrier collection indicates what might be achieved in this respect. A detector designed specifically for good time resolution as, for example, in a time-of-flight experiment, would probably be operated as a $dE/dx$ detector and should have a thin barrier, but not necessarily one which penetrates the whole crystal. With minimum ionizing particles ambipolar effect would not be severe and series resistance could be kept small.

Equation (4.9a) shows that, for this object, a material of low resistivity is required. From eqns. (4.1) and (4.9) it is a simple matter to derive the alternative relationship (for a $P$–$N$ counter):

$$t_c = \frac{2 \cdot 3 X^2}{\mu_p V} \qquad \qquad \ldots (6.1)$$

A suitable counter would have a barrier no deeper than is necessary to obtain a detectable signal; it would be made of low resistivity crystal and would be operated under high bias.

The limits of development in this direction are not immediately apparent but the counters described in 6.7 show that $dE/dx$ detection is feasible for low energy particles using a barrier of only 50 $\mu$, even when the noise level is relatively high. It is reasonable to assume that a barrier 100 $\mu$ deep would be adequate for most purposes and this could be obtained with about 400 V bias, using 120 $\Omega$cm, $P$-type silicon. The theoretical collecting time would be about 1 nsec. In $dE/dx$ detection the initial distribution of excess carriers is approximately uniform and an algebraic analysis of the pulse generation is possible. This has been done for a $P$–$N$ configuration and it is found that the 10–90 per cent rise time is less than one-quarter of the full collecting time, i.e. $2 \cdot 5 \times 10^{-10}$ sec, in this case.

The use of an $N$–$P$ counter and, still more, the use of germanium should improve even on this result. Ambipolar effect would probably prevent all this being realized in practice but a 10–90 per cent rise time less than 1 nsec might well be obtained.

## 6.6 PARTICLE DISCRIMINATION

### (a) Using variable barrier depth

A particle which penetrates through the barrier gives a pulse of lower amplitude than would correspond with its total energy. The facility with which the barrier depth may be altered (either by change of bias or by use of a crystal of suitable base resistivity) makes it possible to discriminate between particles of similar energy but of different range. This is preferable to the use of stopping foils, since it has much less effect on energy resolution. McKenzie reports[13] discrimination of oxygen ions from protons and alphas by this method, and Amsel obtained a factor of two in the pulse heights from alphas and protons of energy 2 MeV, using a barrier of depth less than the proton range.

This technique is described by Amsel *et al.*[3], from which the diagrams below are reproduced. *Figure 6.10* shows three proton peaks

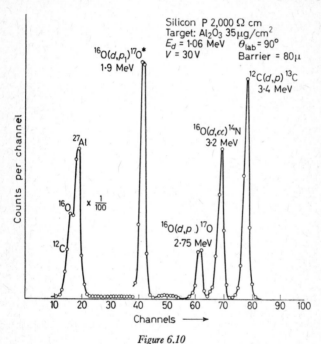

*Figure 6.10*

(G. Amsel, P. Baruch and O. Smulkovski[3], by courtesy of Inst. Radio Engrs, New York)

and one alpha peak in a spectrum obtained with a silicon *P–N* junction counter of high resistivity crystal. The barrier depth with 30 V bias is 80 $\mu$, sufficient to stop all the particles.

*Figure 6.11* shows a spectrum of the same reaction, using an *N–P* counter made from 35 $\Omega$ cm crystal; the barrier is 30 $\mu$. The proton peaks now appear, in reverse order, relatively far down the energy scale and the $\alpha$-peak is isolated. In a case like this, peaks due to

101

particles which are penetrating the barrier would show a shift in their position if the bias is changed by a few per cent, and particles may be identified by this fact alone.

When particles penetrate through the barrier some carrier collection occurs by diffusion from regions just outside the depletion zone

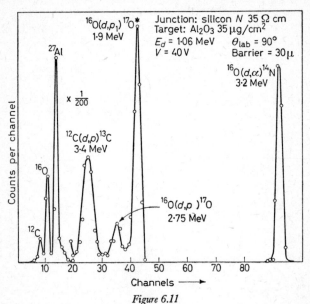

*Figure 6.11*

(G. Amsel, P. Baruch and O. Smulkovski[3], by courtesy of Inst. Radio Engrs, New York)

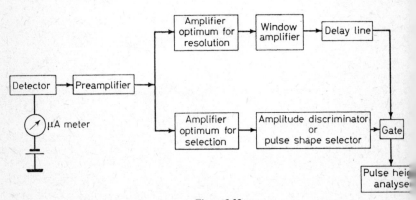

*Figure 6.12*

(G. Amsel, P. Baruch and O. Smulkovski[3], by courtesy of Inst. Radio Engrs, New York)

(see Chapter 4.5). For discrimination it is an advantage to reduce this effect by using short time clipping.

Given a condition in which some particles are penetrating the barrier, it is possible to eliminate them by electronic means, using either amplitude discrimination or by discriminating on the pulse shape. The latter utilizes the fact mentioned above, that with long range particles collection occurs partly by diffusion and this gives a longer rise time. A block diagram of the system suggested by Amsel shown in *Figure 6.12.*

### 6.7   PARTICLE DISCRIMINATION

*(b)   Using dE/dx, E Detection*

In the energy region 10 to 50 MeV it often happens that the discrimination problem is too great for solution by the methods already described. Other expedients must then be adopted, one of which is $dE/dx, E$ detection. This is not only a method of discrimination, it can be regarded as a fundamentally different system of detection.

To a first approximation, in the non-relativistic case, the energy lost by a particle in traversing a given thin layer of matter is proportional to $mZ^2/E$, where $m$ is the particle mass, $Z$ its charge and $E$ its energy. If a particle first traverses a thin detector ('thin' refers to the density in $g/cm^2$) and is afterwards stopped in a thick detector, and if the signal in both cases is linear with the energy absorbed, then the product of the two signals is a measure of the quantity $mZ^2$. A $dE/dx, E$ detector is an assembly of two counters in line, to accomplish this double detection, and the pulse height multiplication is done electronically. Measurement, by this method, of a quantity roughly proportional to $mZ^2$ is a potent tool for particle discrimination, as the expression takes the values 1, 2, 3, 12 and 16 for protons, deuterons, tritons, $^3$He and alphas, respectively. The discriminating circuit described above may be used to operate a gating circuit, by means of which the energy spectrum (the sum of the two signals) of one particular type of particle can be isolated.

Before the advent of semiconductor detectors $dE/dx, E$, counting was necessarily done by older methods; for example, the 'thin' counter could be a small proportional ion chamber and the $E$ counter a scintillator and photomultiplier. Even for particles of moderate energy such a device is rather large, and resolution suffers from non-linearity of the scintillator and from collimation problems due to the relatively long track length needed even in a 'thin' ion chamber.

The use of semiconductors for $dE/dx, E$ detection is described by Wegner[14, 15] by Halbert [16] and also by Braid and Heinrich[17]. The methods employed by the first will be described briefly. The first step was the replacement of the $E$ counter, consisting of a NaI scintillator and photomultiplier, by a 1 cm$^2$ $P$–$N$ junction counter in silicon. This change produced the improvement shown in *Figure 6.13*, which illustrates energy spectra of 21 MeV $^3$He ions, obtained with the two

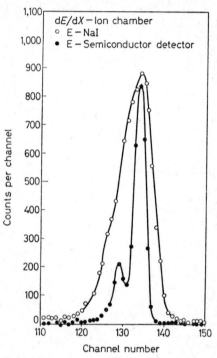

*Figure 6.13. Comparison of resolution obtained in dE/dx, E detectors with E detection: (a) by scintillation methods using a NaI crystal; (b) with a P–N junction counter*

(H. E. Wegner, *Semiconductor Nuclear Particle Detectors*, Nat. Acad. Sci. (Washington), Publ. 871, p. 74)

systems. The double peak is due to an excited state at 0·478 MeV in $^7$Li, and the barrier layer detector gives sufficiently good resolution to enable these two peaks to be studied independently as a function of angle.

Wegner then replaced the ion chamber also, by a barrier layer counter. This was a $P$–$N$ junction d$E$/d$x$ counter in 6,000 $\Omega$cm crystal and was only 0·05 mm thick, with an aperture of 3/16 in. The back contact was made on to a lapped surface with a layer of gold $100\,\mu g/cm^2$ and connexions were made with silver paste. At 5 V bias the depletion layer extended through the entire thickness and the counter had negligible windows. The reverse current remained less than 1 $\mu A$ up to 10 V bias. It should be noted that this very good $dE/dx$ counter probably owes its success to the use of high resistivity crystal and to being exceptionally thin. Because of these two factors,

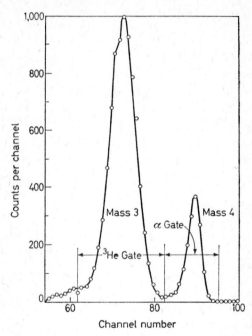

*Figure 6.14. Particle discrimination using semiconductor*
$dE/dx$, $E$ detection

(H. E. Wegner, *Semiconductor Nuclear Particle Detectors*, Nat. Acad. Sci. (Washington), Publ. 871, p. 74)

a full-thickness depletion zone was obtained with very moderate bias, thus keeping the reverse current as low as possible. This further substitution of semiconductor methods gave a slight improvement in particle discrimination; the result is illustrated in *Figure 6.14*, which shows $^3$He and alpha counts analysed by means of the product pulse, as described at the beginning of this chapter.

*Figure 6.15* shows the upper portion of an ungated energy spectrum from the reaction $^{12}C(^3He, \alpha)^{11}C$, obtained with semiconductor $dE/dx$ and $E$ detection.

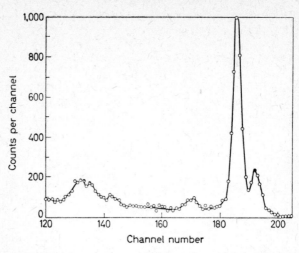

*Figure 6.15. Ungated E spectrum of mixed ³He and α-particles*
(H. E. Wegner, *Semiconductor Nuclear Particle Detectors*, Nat. Acad. Sci. (Washington), Publ. 871, p. 74)

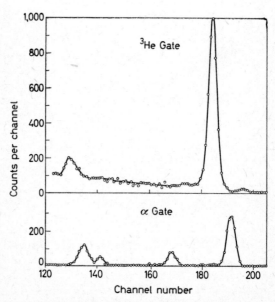

*Figure 6.16. Gated spectra of ³He and α-particles*
(H. E. Wegner, *Semiconductor Nuclear Particle Detectors*, Nat. Acad. Sci. (Washington), Publ. 871, p. 74)

*Figure 6.16* shows gated spectra of the same particles. The $^3$He gate reveals two peaks, corresponding to the ground state and the first excited state of $^{12}$C. The low energy continuum between the peaks is due to $^3$He particles elastically scattered from nuclei other than those in the target, and could be reduced by improved collimation. The small peak on the extreme right is due to elastic scattering from oxygen, present as an impurity. The α-gate gives a very clear spectrum, showing emission from the ground state and the first three excited states of $^{11}$C.

## 6.8   NEUTRON DETECTION

The known reactions of neutrons with silicon and germanium are described by Dearnaley and Whitehead[1]; both materials are relatively inactive with neutrons of low energy. Detection of neutrons

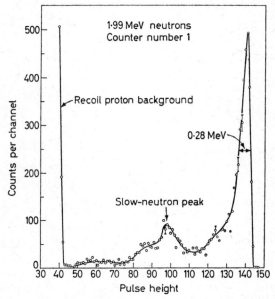

*Figure 6.17. Pulse height spectrum from 1·99 MeV neutrons*
(T. A. Love and R. B. Murrary[18])

with barrier layer counters is achieved using an intermediate reaction and various methods have been reported. The intermediate reactions employed involve the emission of two charged particles, and it is advantageous to detect both. The reactant is therefore used in the form of a thin layer sandwiched closely between the sensitive surfaces of two detectors. With this $4\pi$ geometry maximum collection is ensured and much of the background can be eliminated by coincidence counting.

The reaction, $^{10}B(n, \alpha)^7Li$ has been used (see, for example, Love and Murray[18] and discussion following and Sakai[19]), but the most popular method is the use of the reaction $^6Li(n, \alpha)^3H$. This has been described

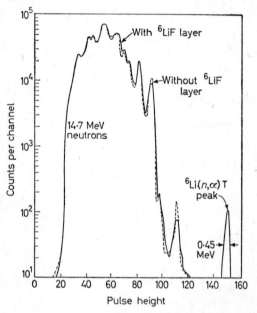

*Figure 6.18. Response to neutrons from the reactions* $^3H(d,n)^4He(14\cdot7 \text{ MeV})$

(G. Dearnaley and A. B. Whitehead[18])

by Love and Murray[20, 18] (presented by Dabbs) and in several other reports, notably by Dearnaley *et al.*[21], Sakai[19] and Bok *et al*,[22] The methods employed by Love and Murray are described below—those of other workers are similar.

Two gold–silicon surface barrier detectors are used, one of which has a central area about 35 mm$^2$ coated with 150 μg/cm$^2$ of lithium fluoride enriched in $^6Li$. The coating is made by vacuum vaporization straight on to the gold surface, and is carefully masked to prevent deposition on the unprotected silicon. The two counters are mounted with their sensitive surfaces parallel and only 0·05 mm away from each other, the mountings being made of non-reactive materials (P.T.F.E.). Coincidence counting is employed; the two pulses are added and the sum-pulse recorded by a pulse height analyser.

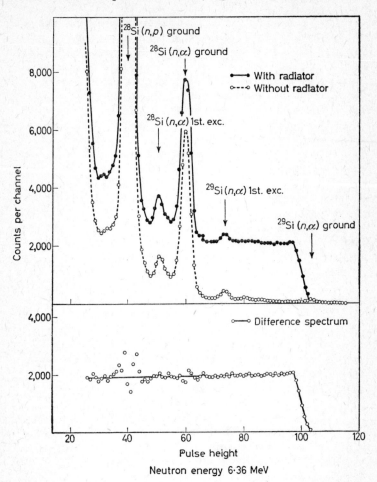

*Figure 6.19. Proton recoil counter: the two upper curves are the spectra from the two sides of the counter separately; the lower diagram shows the pure proton recoil spectrum obtained by electronic difference analysis*

(G. Dearnaley *et al.*[21])

The $Q$ for the reaction is 4·78 MeV but some energy is lost in the fluoride and gold layers. Love and Murray found very good linearity of the sum-pulse height with incident neutron energy plus 4·6 MeV, at least for neutrons up to 3·5 MeV. The results obtained at these energies are illustrated in *Figure 6.17*. The resolution of 0·28 MeV (f.w.h.m.) on the 1·99 MeV peak corresponds very closely to expectation, as calculated from the thickness of the LiF and gold layers and the geometry, involving transmission at high angles. The smaller peak corresponds to an energy of 4·6 MeV and is due to contamination of the flux with slow neutrons. Efficiency is very low, ranging from about $3 \times 10^{-3}$ at thermal energies to $10^{-6}$ at 2 MeV. This could be improved by having a thicker layer of LiF, but only at the cost of reducing the energy resolution. Dearnaley and Whitehead report[1] a resolution of 70 keV for thermal neutrons with their lithium fluoride detector.

At higher neutron energies the reactions with silicon become significant and linearity deteriorates. Even up to 15 MeV the device gives spectra showing a clear peak corresponding to the above linear relationship; below this peak, however, there is a confused spectrum from reactions in silicon. This effect is illustrated in *Figure 6.18*.

A device which is similar in principle but uses gaseous $^3$He as the reactant is being studied at A.E.R.E., Harwell[1]. The reaction, $^3$He$(n,p)^3$H has a larger cross-section for neutrons up to a few MeV and has a $Q$ of only 770 keV. Ajdacic and Lalovic[23] report the use of uranium as the reactant in somewhat similar detector assemblies, to record the neutron flux in a reactor core. They state that the detection of neutrons through the agency of fission fragments is easier than using $\alpha$-particles and tritons from the $^6$Li reaction. In the heavy neutron flux inside the reactor radiation damage was severe, but the method was considered practicable up to $10^9$ n/cm$^2$/sec. The use of uranium (enriched) is also reported by Steinberg[24].

Dearnaley et al.[21] report experiments on the development of a proton recoil neutron spectrometer. A circular disk of $N$-type silicon has two separate semicircular areas coated with gold, thus forming twin counters of identical properties. One of these is covered by a plastic film, which forms the 'hydrogenous radiator'. Simultaneous analysis is used and, in each channel, the difference in the number of counts is recorded electrically. The detector is illustrated in the frontispiece and some results are shown in *Figure 6.19*.

## 6.9  $\beta$-PARTICLE SPECTROMETRY

$\beta$-particles of energy exceeding about 30 keV will give a detectable signal in a good barrier layer detector, suitably biased. At this energy the signal barely emerges from the noise level. At higher energies, and provided the barrier is greater than the particle range, a 'total energy' peak is obtained together with a continuum covering the lower energy range of the spectrum. This low energy 'tail' is due to back-scattering of the particles, as a result of which some leave the detector before losing all their energy. These effects can be seen in the 300 keV spectrum of *Figure 6.20*[8].

If the β-particle range (the end point) exceeds the barrier depth by a moderate amount, a total absorption peak is still obtained but its height is reduced. This is because some of the particles undergo sufficient deflexion that they remain in the barrier layer until they are stopped. The particles which penetrate right through the barrier lose varying amounts of energy, depending on the extent to which they are

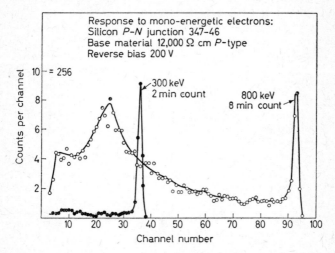

*Figure 6.20. The response of a high resistivity junction counter to mono-energetic electrons*

(J. M. McKenzie and G. T. Ewan[8], by courtesy of Inst. Radio Engrs, New York)

deflected, and contribute to the tail of the spectrum, which therefore increases in height. With a further increase in beta range a second peak begins to appear which is due to particles passing through the barrier with little or no deflexion. This is termed the 'minimum ionization peak' and is seen in the 800 keV curve of *Figure 6.20*. It should be noted that this spectrum is derived from a much larger number of particles than that for 300 keV, a fact which is readily apparent from a comparison of their areas. The barrier depth in this case was about 500 μ the end point ranges for the 300 and 800 keV β-particles are about 300 and 1,300 μ respectively.

With still further increase in beta energy the two peaks move further apart, the minimum ionization energy growing less owing to

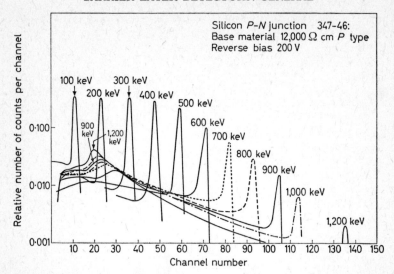

*Figure 6.21. The response of the junction to the same number of electrons in the energy range from 100 keV to 1,200 keV. The thickness of the depletion region corresponds to an electron range of 350 keV. A total absorption peak due to the high scattering of electrons exists to an electron energy of 1,200 keV*

(J. M. McKenzie and G. T. Ewan[8], by courtesy of Inst. Radio Engrs, New York)

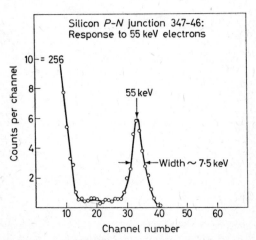

*Figure 6.22. The response of a silicon P–N junction to 55 keV electrons showing 7·5 keV resolution. Detector noise becomes appreciable below 20 keV*

(J. M. McKenzie and G. T. Ewan[8], by courtesy of Inst. Radio Engrs, New York)

112

reduced multiple scattering. Also, the minimum ionization peak grows larger, while the total energy peak grows smaller until it can no longer be detected. This effect is shown in *Figure 6.21*.

A very similar series of experiments, with very similar results, is reported by Gunnersen *et al.*[25], who used surface barrier detectors.

The total absorption peak gives very good linearity with energy, even when the range exceeds the barrier depth by a factor up to 9 or 10. Resolution, also, appears to be reasonably good. The 300 keV peak in *Figure 6.20* is relatively well defined by experimental points. By scaling on the diagram this peak is found to be about 16 keV at half height. Another result, at lower energy, is illustrated in *Figure 6.22*[8]. The efficiency, however, is inferior to that of an ionization counter, even when operating within the barrier depth. This is due to a substantial proportion (∼ 30 per cent) of the incident particles being back-scattered and lost.

## 6.10  γ-SPECTROMETRY

γ-rays can be detected by virtue of Compton electrons, photoelectrons or pair production; i.e. the particle detected is the moving electron, which produces carrier pairs as for β-rays. Because of the low atomic

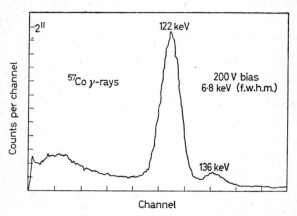

Figure 6.23. *Response of a junction detector to*
*γ-rays from* ⁵⁷Co

(G. L. Miller [26])

number of silicon the efficiency is low, especially for photoelectrons, and a deep barrier is needed. In detectors having barriers 0·8 mm deep γ-rays giving photoelectrons of range less than this distance have been detected with good energy resolution. This corresponds to energies less than 550 or 600 keV. Since pair production requires a minimum energy of 1·02 MeV it plays no part in this case.

For γ-rays there is no back-scattering problem but a substantial low energy tail appears in the spectrum, due to Compton electrons and to some of the photoelectrons produced near to the edge of the barrier which escape full detection. *Figure 6.23*[26] shows this tail. The peak produced is, of course, the total energy peak due to photoelectrons, and has the expected pulse-height energy relationship.

Gamma detection is also reported by Donovan[27], who mentions resolution of 6·5 keV (presumably f.w.h.m.), limited by electronic noise. It is to be expected that germanium counters would show some advantage over silicon, at least in efficiency, by reason of the higher atomic number. This, however, does not appear to have been investigated as yet. The possibilities of barrier layer counters for health physics monitoring are reviewed by Jones[28].

## 6.11 RADIATION DAMAGE

There is an extensive literature on the effects of radiation damage in semiconductors, particularly silicon and germanium, and the effects on the behaviour of barrier layer counters are specifically considered[29, 1]. Radiation of any kind induces lattice defects, and charged particles also contaminate the crystal to some extent. The most important effect is the reduction in carrier lifetime, but there are significant effects on the resistivity. The latter is usually an increase, because the vast majority of the new localized energy levels are deeper in the energy gap than the donor or acceptor levels and therefore act as compensators. With prolonged irradiation over-compensation can sometimes occur, converting to high resistivity material of the opposite type. In addition to these general effects, radiation may have specific effects if it favours the production of one or two particular types of defect. The result then depends on the energy level of the local electron states concerned in relation to that of the conduction and valence bands.

Semiconductor detectors therefore deteriorate in use, or if otherwise exposed to radiation. If the flux concerned is moderate a barrier layer counter will maintain acceptable stability for a long time. This is probably because there is usually a substantial margin between the carrier lifetime when new and the minimum lifetime needed for full collection. The reduction in lifetime caused by radiation is shown first by increased reverse current, with a consequent increase in detector noise, and later by further loss of resolution due to incomplete collection. Multiple peaking is a common symptom in bad cases. This arises from the presence of a particular zone in the sensitive volume where there is exceptionally low carrier lifetime. If the particle track passes through this region incomplete collection causes the signal to have less than the normal amplitude. Klingensmith[30] reports experiments with fast neutrons on surface barrier detectors in 3,000 $\Omega$cm crystal at a low bias of 6 V. Since, under these conditions, the bias is barely high enough for good collection it is to be expected that the effects of radiation damage would be observed relatively quickly. Deterioration in $\alpha$-particle resolution became apparent after irradiation with $5 \times 10^{11}$ fast n/cm$^2$. After further irradiation multiple peaking developed and the mean pulse height was much reduced after $10^{13}$ n/cm$^2$. Curtis et al.[31] investigated neutron effects in germanium and found that damage was small up to $10^{11}$/cm$^2$. They also investigated the effects of $\gamma$-rays (1·17 and 1·33 MeV) and found damage becoming appreciable at $10^{14}$/cm$^2$.

Dearnaley and Whitehead[1] investigated the effects of 5·5 MeV $\alpha$-particles (from $^{241}$Am) in 1,000 $\Omega$cm surface barrier detectors. To make the effects readily apparent they, too, used a very low bias of 2 V. A slight increase in reverse current was found after exposure to $10^8$/cm$^2$ and further increase to the large figure of 3 $\mu$A/cm$^2$ occurred with exposure to $10^{11}$/cm$^2$. There was a significant variation around these figures for different detectors. The initial reverse current at 2 V bias was, of course, very small. If it is assumed that the increase was not due to surface leakage, it follows that the lifetime had been reduced to about 1 $\mu$sec by this exposure. Resolution, initially 1·5 per cent (f.w.h.m.), began to deteriorate at $2 \times 10^9$/cm$^2$ and secondary peaks appeared on further irradiation. After $10^{11}$/cm$^2$ the resolution in different counters had reached 6–15 per cent. At this stage an increase in bias to 20 V gave improved resolution of 3–4 per cent and eliminated the multiple peaking.

It is possible that controlled radiation damage may be exploited in the future, to produce particular effects; for example, it may be possible to obtain very high resistivity by compensation without paying an unacceptable price in reduced carrier lifetime.

## 6.12 SPECIAL CONFIGURATIONS

One important feature of barrier layer counters is the facility with which special configurations can be made to suit particular applications. Some of these have already been mentioned and some others are briefly described in this section.

*Annular counter*—This, as its name implies, is a large area barrier layer detector with a central hole. It was used by Bromley[6] to give symmetrical detection at angles very near to 180° C. The accelerated particles are collimated through the central hole from the back of the detector and strike a target situated on the axis at a suitable distance, depending on the geometry required.

*Multiple counter*—This can most easily be made by using surface barrier techniques. The surface coating is applied through a comb of fine wires and connexions are made separately to each surface element thus obtained. The technique is only successful with silicon, because the surface conductivity of germanium results in mutual response of adjacent sections. Such detectors in silicon have been operated[1] successfully with elements separated by only 0·1 mm. This configuration is of obvious interest for use with a magnetic analyser, or for scattering experiments.

*Fission detector*—If a thin film of fissile material is sandwiched between a pair of counters (in the manner described for neutron detection in Chapter 6·8) a fission product spectrum may be obtained,

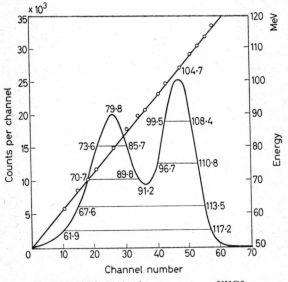

*Figure 6.24. Fission fragment spectrum of* $^{252}$Cf

(G. L. Miller[35])

using coincidence counting. One result, due to Miller[35] is shown in *Figure 6.24* and similar experiments are described [2, 32 and 33]. Comparison of results obtained in these experiments with those obtained by other methods, notably time-of-flight measurements, shows an 'ionization defect' which was thought at first to be due to a significant window for these heavy particles. This possibility has not been definitely eliminated but Walter et al.[34] have shown that, in their experiments, it is primarily due to incomplete collection and is attributed to recombination in the concentrated plasma along the particle track, during the period of delay in collection arising from ambipolar effect. (See also Chapter 10.8.)

Melkonian[36] and Gooding[37] used this method to study fission of $^{235}$U and obtained mass spectra as good as those obtainable by any other method. It was possible to study the influence of neutron energy on the reaction. Mention is made of further work using arrays of three counters to study ternary fission[36].

*Integral* d$E$/d$x$ $E$ *detector*—This is no more than a suggestion (Bromley[6]) at present. It is proposed that a *P–N* junction first be made, and that the surface *N* layer be coated with gold and a third contact applied. This would produce a very thin surface barrier d$E$/d$x$ detector, integral with a junction-type *E* detector. There are obvious problems, but if successful it would be a useful device for discrimination at low energies.

*Carrier multiplication*—The fact that barrier layer detectors give rather a small signal is, at best, an inconvenience, since low-noise high gain amplification is necessary. In some possible applications, such as portable contamination monitoring devices, this nullifies the advantages of small size and low cost in the detector itself.

When operated at 20° K or less, ordinary barrier layer counters exhibit carrier multiplication. This is because the absence of lattice scattering enables the carriers to be accelerated by the field to a speed sufficient for secondary carrier pairs to be formed, a process very similar to that occurring in a proportional counter. The phenomenon has been investigated by Walter, Dabbs and Roberts[38] who reported a direct gain in pulse height by a factor of about 5, but energy resolution was relatively poor. This process, however, is of little interest as a practical method of overcoming the low signal problem.

A similar phenomenon occurs at higher temperatures if the applied field is sufficiently high ($6 \times 10^4$ V/cm for silicon) to overcome the 'lattice drag'. Fields of this order can sometimes be obtained in barrier layers without breakdown and the results have been investigated by Chynoweth[39]. It was found possible, without great difficulty, to obtain multiplication by a factor of about 10, but resolution was poor. The problems arise from inhomogeneities in the crystal, leading to variations in the multiplication obtained.

In the discussion following Chynoweth's paper[39] Rediker mentioned a G-M type operation, comparable to that of an avalanche transistor, which he obtained in compensated germanium at 42° K.

The breakdown bias was 100 V but the current could then be sustained at 50 V. If the bias is set between these limits an incident particle (or illumination) will trigger the device. A current of 1 A could be obtained, triggered by a single particle in this way.

*Transistor detector*—A more hopeful approach to a solution of the problem of signal size is to provide integral amplification by fabricating the detector as a transistor. This is described by Williams and Webb[40, 41] and their counter is illustrated in *Figure 6.25*, below. The crystal used was 20,000 $\Omega$cm $P$-type silicon, and had $N$ layers made on both faces by phosphorus diffusion. The bias is adjusted so that the depletion layer extends nearly through the crystal, leaving a narrow $P$ layer between it and the $N$ layer at the back. When a particle enters, holes are swept into this thin $P$ layer, which acts as the base of the

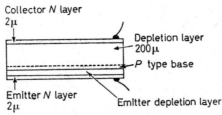

*Figure 6.25. Transistor detector*

transistor configuration, and current amplification is obtained. A gain of up to 1,000 has been obtained and the signal-to-noise ratio ranged from 50 to 180, depending on size (200–30 mm², respectively). Energy resolution was only 15 per cent (f.w.h.m.) for 5 MeV $\alpha$-particles.

The duration of the current pulse depends on the lifetime of the excess holes in the base and was in the region of 30 μsec so that time resolution also is much reduced by comparison with the ordinary method of detector and amplifier. In some applications, however, this could be accepted and substantial improvements can be expected with further development. It seems that this is a case which requires optimization of carrier lifetime.

*Side entry*—One obvious method of overcoming the limitations imposed by small barrier depth is to use a side face of the counter as aperture, so that the particle tracks are parallel to the plane of the junction. Some exploratory work in this direction has been done by Koch, Messier and Valin[42, 43], who also made their detectors in a different manner. They used 1,000 $\Omega$cm $P$-type silicon (which is termed by them 'nearly intrinsic') and diffused boron into one side and phosphorus into the other, thus obtaining high conductivity $P$

and $N$ faces with low conductivity crystal in between. They termed this a '$P.I.N.$' configuration, i.e. $P$-type:Intrinsic:$N$-type, but it hardly seems to justify the description, which is reserved by the writer for another type of detector to be described in Chapter 7.

Koch *et al.* used only a small crystal, 1 mm × 0·8 mm × 280 μm and diffused to depths of about 80 μ on both faces. Under a bias of 70 V the depletion zone was extended through the region of the remaining low conductivity material (about 120 μ) and further increase in bias produced no further change in capacitance. This relationship between bias and depletion depth corresponds roughly with Blankenship's nomograph, so it does not appear that anything was gained in this respect by the deep boron and phosphorus diffusions. However, this technique must give very much better ohmic contacts than are normally obtained on barrier layer detectors and could be useful in preventing variation of capacitance with bias above a certain minimum.

The use of side entry with small sensitive volumes demands a very high standard of collimation and Koch *et al.* refer to reduced resolution due to particles entering the diffusion zones, where loss of carriers is high due to slow collection and low carrier lifetime. Good linearity with particle energy was obtained for α-particles and γ-photons. Resolution was 2 per cent (f.w.h.m.) for 40 MeV alphas and 8 per cent on the photo-electron peak for gammas of 280 keV.

*Stacked detectors*—This is another idea which has not yet been attempted. In order to obtain a deep sensitive volume a pile of windowless detectors, of d$E$/d$x$ configuration described earlier, might be employed. If they were sufficiently similar in their properties they could be connected in series, or they could be connected to separate supplies and their outputs added electronically. Bilaniuk's proposal for identifying their outputs by the use of delay lines may also be useful in some applications; for example, the approximate measurement of range.

A stack of detectors, as described above, might be employed with side entry. It would then be possible to obtain some information, in two dimensions, on the track of a high energy particle passing through them. The idea might be extended by employing detectors in hodoscopic arrays, thus obtaining three-dimensional information[6].

## REFERENCES

[1] DEARNALEY, G. and WHITEHEAD, A. B., *A.E.R.E. Rep.* R-3662 (1961)
[2] FRIEDLAND, S. S., MAYER, J. W. and WIGGINS, J. S., *Proceedings of Seventh Scintillation Counter Symposium*, Inst. Radio Engrs. N.Y., N.S.7, Nos. 2 and 3 (Sept. 1960) p. 181

[3] AMSEL, G., BARUCH, P. and SMULKOVSKI, O., *Solid State Radiation Detectors*, Inst. Radio Engrs, N.Y., N.S.8, No. 1 (Jan. 1961) p. 21

[4] FANO, U., *Phys. Rev.* 72 (1947) 26

[5] BLANKENSHIP, J. L. and BORKOWSKI, C. J., *Proceedings of Seventh Scintillation Counter Symposium*, Inst. Radio Engrs, N.Y., N.S.7, Nos. 2 and 3 (Sept. 1960) p. 190

[6] BROMLEY, D. A., *Semiconductor Nuclear Particle Detectors*, Nat. Acad. Sci. (Washington), Publ. 871, p. 61

[7] BLANKENSHIP, J. L., *ibid.* p. 43

[8] MCKENZIE, J. M. and EWAN, G. T., *Solid State Radiation Detectors*, Inst. Radio Engrs, N.Y., N.S.8, No. 1 (Jan. 1961) p. 50

[9] AMSEL, G. and SMULKOVSKI, O., *C. R. Acad. Sci.*, Paris, T251 (1960) p. 950

[10] BILANIUK, O. M. and MARSH, B. B., *Proceedings of a Conference on Nuclear Electronics* (May 1961), I.A.E.A.

[11] CHETHAM-STRODE, A., TARRANT, J. R. and SILVA, R. J., *Solid State Radiation Detectors*, Inst. Radio Engrs, N.Y., N.S.8, No. 1 (Jan. 1961) p. 59

[12] FOX, R. J., *Semiconductor Nuclear Particle Detectors*, Nat. Acad. Sci. (Washington), Publ. 871, App. B

[13] MCKENZIE, J. M., *Bull. Amer. phys. Soc.* 5, No. 5 (1960)

[14] WEGNER, H. E., *Semiconductor Nuclear Particle Detectors*, Nat. Acad. Sci. (Washington), Publ. 871, p. 74

[15] WEGNER, H. E., *Proceedings of a Conference on Nuclear Electronics*, (May 1961), I.A.E.A.

[16] HALBERT, M. L., *ibid.*

[17] BRAID, T. and HEINRICH, J., *ibid.*

[18] LOVE, T. A. and MURRAY, R. B., *Semiconductor Nuclear Particle Detectors*, Nat. Acad. Sci. (Washington), Publ. 871, p. 196

[19] SAKAI, E., *Proceedings of a Conference on Nuclear Electronics* (May 1961), I.A.E.A.

[20] LOVE, T. A. and MURRAY, R. B., *Solid State Radiation Detectors*, Inst. Radio Engrs, N.Y., N.S.8, No. 1 (Jan. 1961) p. 91

[21] DEARNALEY, G., FERGUSON, A. T. G., WHITEHEAD, A. B. and MONTAGUE, J., *Proceedings of a Conference on Nuclear Electronics*, (May 1961), I.A.E.A.

[22] BOK, J. and DE COSNAC, B., *ibid.*

[23] AJDACIC, V. and LALOVIC, B., *ibid.*

[24] STEINBERG, R., *Nucleonics* 18, 2 (1960) p. 85

[25] GUNNERSEN, E., DUNMUR, I. and GEORGE, G., *Proceedings of a Conference on Nuclear Electronics* (May 1961), I.A.E.A.

[26] MILLER, G. L., *Semiconductor Nuclear Particle Detectors*, Nat. Acad. Sci. (Washington), Publ. 871, p. 19

[27] DONOVAN, P. F., MILLER, G. L. and FOREMAN, B. M., *Bull. Amer. phys. Soc.* 5 (1960) 355

[28] JONES, A. R., *Nucleonics* 18, 10 (1960) p. 86

[29] WERTHIER, C. K., *Semiconductor Nuclear Particle Detectors*, Nat. Acad. Sci. (Washington) Publ. 871, p. 128

# REFERENCES

[30] KLINGENSMITH, R. W., *Solid State Radiation Detectors*, Inst. Radio Engrs, N.Y., N.S. 8, No. 1 (Jan. 1961) p. 112

[31] CURTIS, O. L. *et al.*, *J. appl. Phys.* 28 (1957) 1161

[32] MILLER, G. L., BROWN, W. L., DONOVAN, P. F. and MACKINTOSH, J. M., *Proceedings of Seventh Scintillation Counter Symposium*, Inst. Radio Engrs, N.Y., N.S.7, Nos. 2 and 3 (Sept. 1960) p. 185

[33] JOYNER, W. T., SCHMITT, H. W., NEILER, J. H. and SILVA, R. L., *Solid State Radiation Detectors*, Inst. Radio Engrs, N.Y., N.S.8, No. 1 (Jan. 1961) p. 54

[34] WALTER, F. J., DABBS, J. W. T. and ROBERTS, L. D., *Proceedings of a Conference on Nuclear Electronics* (May 1961), I.A.E.A.

[35] MILLER, G. L. and GIBSON, W. M., *ibid.*

[36] MELKONIAN, E., *A.E.R.E. Rep.* R-3524 (1960)

[37] GOODING, T. R., *Proc. phys. Soc. Lond.* 77, 5 (1961) 1097

[38] WALTER, F. J., DABBS, J. W. T. and ROBERTS, L. D., *Solid State Radiation Detectors*, Inst. Radio Engrs, N.Y., N.S.8, No. 1 (Jan. 1961)

[39] CHYNOWETH, A. G., *Semiconductor Nuclear Particle Detectors*, Nat. Acad. Sci. (Washington), Publ. 871, p. 171

[40] WILLIAMS, R. L. and WEBB, P. P., *ibid.* p. 182

[41] WILLIAMS, R. L. and WEBB, P. P., *Solid State Radiation Detectors*, Inst. Radio Engrs, N.Y., N.S.8, No. 1, (Jan. 1961)

[42] KOCH, L., MESSIER, J. and VALIN, J., *Semiconductor Nuclear Particle Detectors*, Nat. Acad. Sci. (Washington), Publ. 871, p. 52

[43] KOCH, L., MESSIER, J. and VALIN, J., *Solid State Radiation Detectors*, Inst. Radio Engrs, N.Y., N.S.8, No. 1 (Jan. 1961) p. 43

# 7

# *P.I.N.* DETECTORS

## 7.1 INTRODUCTION

A *P.I.N.* detector consists of a layer of intrinsic crystal sandwiched between $P$ and $N$ surface layers. This very recent development could be regarded as a special configuration of the diffused junction type, but is described in some detail here because it appears to be of considerable importance and involves an entirely new technique. The value of the new technique lies in the fact that it offers an extension of the barrier layer depth by a factor up to five, and still further increase may be possible. It thus combines the virtues of the barrier layer type (low dark current and operation at ambient temperature) with those of the bulk counter. The development is still very much in its infancy and only one method of preparation has yet been reported.

## 7.2 THE LITHIUM ION DRIFT TECHNIQUE

The first investigation of the process involved, with a view to its use in making a counter, is described by Pell[1]. Lithium is a donor impurity in silicon, giving $E_D = 0.03$ eV, but it differs from the usual doping agents employed (e.g. boron, phosphorus, gallium) in being an interstitial impurity. Because of this difference it has a diffusion coefficient higher by a factor of $10^7$ and it is relatively easy to make deep diffused junctions. Crystals of $P$-type silicon are employed with a low resistivity of $1-1,000$ $\Omega$cm. The size and shape may vary over wide limits but the thickness should not exceed 6 mm. One surface is coated with a 30 per cent suspension of lithium in oil, and dried in nitrogen at 200 to 250° C. Diffusion is then carried out at higher temperatures up to 600° C for times ranging between 1 min and 1 h, depending on the resistivity of the silicon. The junction should then be at a depth of about 100 $\mu$ or more, and will have the form illustrated in *Figure 7.1*. In this diagram, the horizontal axis is drawn at the level where the impurity concentration is zero, and the junction therefore occurs at the point marked '$d$'.

When a deep junction has been formed as described above, surface contacts are applied to the crystal by one of several alternative methods. Mayer *et al.*[2] employed soldering to an electroless nickel coating for both contacts; alternatively, both contacts may be alloyed with gold. The crystal is immersed in a bath of silicone oil at some controlled temperature between $120-250°$ C and uniformity of temperature ensured by rapid stirring. The lithium drift process is then

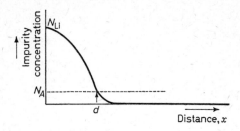

*Figure 7.1. Surface diffusion with lithium*

carried out by applying a reverse bias of $10-300$ V for a controlled time. At these temperatures the lithium ions are mobile and, since they come under the influence of the applied field, they drift into the depleted zone. It was pointed out by Pell that, to a first approximation, this results in a lithium ion concentration having a long 'plateau' at a level which just compensates the acceptor centres, as shown in *Figure 7.2*. This can readily be understood by considering what would

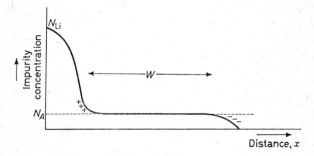

*Figure 7.2. Lithium ion drift under reverse bias*

happen if the concentration ever developed the form shown in *Figure 7.3*. Because of the space charge distribution at a junction under reverse bias (see Chapters 3.3 and 4.5) the strongest electric field exists in the region marked A, and consequently lithium ions would drift preferentially away from this region, thereby reducing the irregularity in the distribution and eroding it away to the form of *Figure 7.2.*

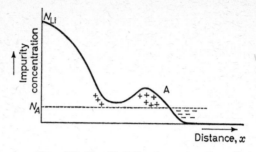

*Figure 7.3. Unstable lithium ion concentration*

## 7.3 LIMITATIONS OF THE DRIFT PROCESS

The process of ion drift briefly described above therefore results in the production of a layer of crystal which is rendered intrinsic by compensation. The depth of this layer can be controlled, within limits, by controlling the time, temperature and bias applied. The theory[3] of the process is reasonably well understood and predictions agree quite well with results obtained. On the basis of the simple description given above, it would appear that there is no limit to the width of the intrinsic zone obtainable, it being necessary only to ensure that the supply of lithium from the surface does not become exhausted. However, a limit is imposed by the effects of carrier generation current, as will be seen below.

The drift velocity of the lithium ions during the process is determined by the simple relation

$$v = \mu_L . F$$

where $\mu_L$ is the drift mobility of the ions at the temperature concerned and $F$ the local electric field. The ions moving in the intrinsic zone must all have the same velocity, otherwise pile-up of the type shown in *Figure 7.3* would occur. It follows that the ions distribute themselves in such a way as to make the field constant, under the conditions prevailing during the drift process. It is this law, the maintenance of constant field, which really determines the form of the lithium ion concentration. The space charge distribution needed to give a uniform field over the 'intrinsic' zone during drift is shown schematically in *Figure 7.4(a)*. There must be no net space charge in the ion-drift region, consequently the negative space charge due to filled acceptor centres must be exactly neutralized by positive space charge, as shewn

124

by the heavy line. If there were no reverse current the lithium distribution of *Figure 7.2* would follow directly from this. In fact, at the high temperature used for the drift process there is a large bulk reverse current, the dominant component being due to carrier generation in the 'intrinsic' zone. These carriers, when moving under a uniform field, contribute space charge of the linear form shown in *Figure 7.4(b)*. The lithium ion concentration must compensate the space charge of 4(b) in order to give the distribution of 4(a), and therefore

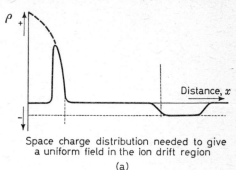

Space charge distribution needed to give
a uniform field in the ion drift region

*Figure 7.4*

(a)

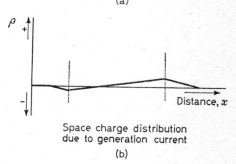

Space charge distribution
due to generation current

(b)

has the form of *Figure 7.5*. This approximates to *Figure 7.2* for an 'intrinsic' zone of small depth, but as the depth increases the compensation becomes less accurate in the deeper parts of the zone.

It can be shown without difficulty that the space charge concentration due to generation current at the $P$ edge of the zone (where it is a maximum) is given approximately by

$$\rho_p = \frac{gW^2}{\mu_p V} \quad \text{electron charges/cm}^3$$

where $W$ is the width of the intrinsic zone, $g$ the generation rate of carrier pairs per unit volume in this zone and $V$ the bias appearing across the zone. As the depth of ion drift increases this rises according to a square law, and no further ion drift will occur when the value of this space charge concentration approaches the concentration $N_A$, of acceptors in the parent crystal. In fact, a practical limit arises before this stage is reached.

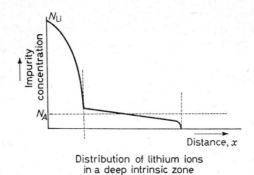

Distribution of lithium ions
in a deep intrinsic zone

*Figure 7.5*

To overcome the problems arising from carrier generation current much can be done by completing the drift process at a lower temperature, and aging after drift is also beneficial[2]. However, with present techniques, the limit of depletion zone depth obtainable is in the region of 4–5 mm.

## 7.4 CHARACTERISTICS

In a *P.I.N.* detector the sensitive zone is primarily determined by the depth of the nominally intrinsic layer and is therefore nearly constant. The characteristics of these counters, therefore, differ profoundly from those of barrier layer counters. The capacitance and the limits of linearity are simple functions of $W$ and are almost independent of applied bias. The capacitance, in e.s.u., is $\epsilon A/4\pi W$. The reverse current at high bias has a significant component due to surface leakage, but in a deep detector at low bias the carrier generation current is dominant and is nearly constant (independent of applied volts). Mayer gives some curves for a counter made in $9\ \Omega$ cm silicon between successive stages of ion drift, and these are reproduced in *Figure 7.6*. The uppermost curve, corresponding to $W = 1.23$ mm, shows reverse current varying from 1·6 to 2·4 $\mu$A/cm$^2$ with bias ranging from 0 to 50 V.

The parent crystal selected for this purpose must be of relatively low resistivity, otherwise it behaves as an intrinsic crystal at high temperatures and no barrier forms. The fact that a practical deep barrier detector can be made from a crystal of low resistivity (which is relatively plentiful) is an advantage in some respects but it means that carrier lifetime is lower to begin with and, with the deeper barriers, there is no longer very much margin of lifetime over collecting time.

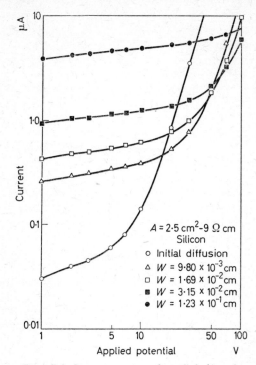

*Figure 7.6. Reverse current and applied bias for different intrinsic zone depths*

(J. W. Mayer, N. A. Bailey and H. L. Dunlap [2])

Effective carrier lifetimes of 1 to 25 µsec are given by Mayer, calculated from the reverse current by the relationship,

$$I = q.g.W = q.n_i.W/2\tau$$

The collecting time is strongly dependent on bias and, on the assumption of a uniform field across the sensitive zone, is

$$t_c = \frac{W^2}{\mu_p.V}$$

For $W = 4$ mm and bias of 100 V, this gives $t_c = 4$ µsec. Collection, however, appears to be better than would be expected from these

127

figures, probably because the carriers under collection have better lifetimes than the 'effective' figure obtained from the reverse current.

It is not possible, by these techniques, to make a counter with windowless performance on its $N$ face, and most of those discussed in this section have relatively thick windows. However, it is possible, if the crystal is not too thick, to drift the lithium ions right through it and obtain approximately windowless performance at the $P$ face. Also, the depth of the intrinsic zone can be made large enough to give satisfactory apertures for many purposes using side entry. The performance is then windowless, and this geometry has further advantages. With side entry the limit of linear response depends on the maximum crystal dimension obtainable with satisfactory uniform properties and (since high basic resistivity is not a requirement) this can be 4 or 5 cm, or more.

Ion drift counters tend to be slightly unstable with time, due to the lithium ions having some small mobility even at ambient temperatures. On storage after manufacture the capacitance increases and becomes more bias dependent. This effect, however, can be prevented by keeping the counters under bias of 50 to 100 V, or by placing them under this bias for several days, when recovery occurs.

## 7.5 PERFORMANCE

Not many reports are yet available on *P.I.N.* counters. The results reproduced here are by Mayer *et al.*[2], who record a general investigation of their potentialities. In most cases interpretation of the results is impeded by lack of full data on the detectors and the conditions of the experiment. It is inferred from the reference that the detectors were relatively large in aperture, between 1·8 and 4·9 cm², and must therefore have had large reverse currents. The results for charged particles are therefore by no means the best obtainable as regards energy resolution. *Figure 7.7* shows the response, to long range protons, of a detector with $W$ approximately 4·5 mm. Resolution (not stated) is adversely affected by the thick window and by noise from the high reverse current.

The windowless performance obtained by drifting through to the back contact is shown in *Figure 7.8*. W was about 1 mm and the radiation was uncollimated $\alpha$-particles of 6 and 8·78 MeV from $^{212}$Pb. No significant window was found for particles entering the $P$ face.

A $\gamma$-detector of small size is badly needed for many applications, to replace ion chambers or scintillation counters. The performance of *P.I.N.* counters is therefore of considerable interest. *Figure 7.9* shows the response of a detector of area 3 cm² and $W = 2$ mm to photons of

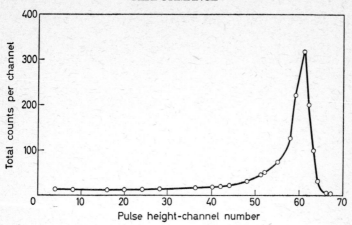

*Figure 7.7. Response of a deep P.I.N. detector to 28 MeV protons*
(J. W. Mayer, N. A. Bailey and H. L. Dunlap [2])

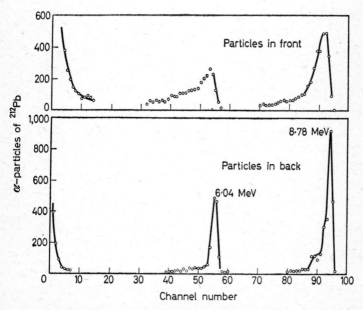

*Figure 7.8. Windowless detection at the P face using a detector of W about 1 mm*

(J. W. Mayer, N. A. Bailey and H. L. Dunlap [2])

662 keV. The spectrum is dominated by Compton electrons but a well-resolved photopeak is obtained on a long count. The relationship between the position of the photopeak and the Compton edge is

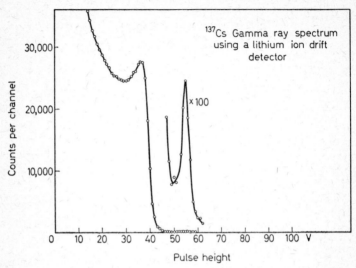

*Figure 7.9. Response to γ-rays of energy 662* keV

(J. W. Mayer, N. A. Bailey and H. L. Dunlap [2])

correct. Mayer and his co-workers give the following results from another counter of $W = 1 \cdot 4$ mm:

TABLE 7.1. GAMMA DETECTION WITH A *P.I.N.* COUNTER

| Source | c/min./mr/hr/cm² of detector area | c/min./μc/cm² |
|--------|-----------------------------------|---------------|
| $^{60}$Co | 280 | |
| $^{137}$Cs | 280 | |
| $^{131}$I | 850 | |
| $^{131}$I ($\beta$ and $\gamma$) | | 310 (source 10 cm from counter) |
| $^{32}$P | | $3 \cdot 84 \times 10^4$ (source 2 cm from counter) |

The response to mono-energetic $\beta$-particles is shown in *Figure 7.10*. As in the case of simple barrier layer detectors (see Chapter 6.9) there is a total energy peak and a high tail. When the range (end point) exceeds $W$, a minimum ionization peak is seen and the total energy counts decrease. The advantage of the deeper sensitive zone is seen in the easy detection of a total energy peak at 1,800 keV, and resolution is good. Two millimetres of silicon is approximately the end point range for a 1 MeV electron.

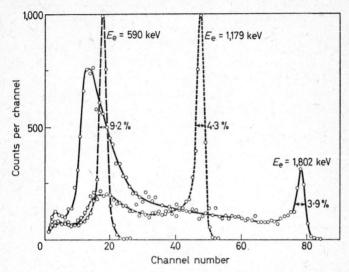

*Figure 7.10. β-radiation detected with a P.I.N. counter 2 mm deep*
(J. W. Mayer, N. A. Bailey and H. L. Dunlap [2])

## REFERENCES

[1] PELL, E. M., *Semiconductor Nuclear Particle Detectors*, Nat. Acad. Sci. (Washington), Publ. 871, p. 136
[2] MAYER, J. W., BAILY, N. A. and DUNLAP, H. L., *Proceedings of a Conference on Nuclear Electronics* (May 1961), I.A.E.A.
[3] PELL, E. M., *J. appl. Phys.* 31 (1960) 291

# 8

# A SEMICONDUCTOR ELECTRON MULTIPLIER

THIS novel idea, is due to and described by White[1, 2]. It has been made the subject of a separate chapter because its principles are entirely different from those of other semiconductor devices.

The electron multiplier performs the same functions, using the same physical principles, as the dynode assembly of a photomultiplier, but has a very much simpler construction. The device is illustrated in *Figure 8.1*; two thin wafers of silicon of very high resistivity are set up parallel to each other and about 1 mm apart, their dimensions being

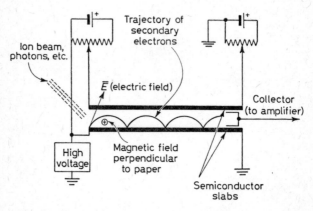

*Figure 8.1. Schematic diagram of electron multiplier (longitudinal section)*

(F. A. White[1])

about 2·5 cm × 2 cm wide × 0·5 mm thick. The silicon used by White was gold-compensated *N*-type, as described in Chapter 2.5, and had a resistivity of about $10^5$ $\Omega$cm. This was increased to $10^7$ $\Omega$cm by cooling. A high electric field is set up between these wafers, its direction being as indicated by the vector $E$ in the diagram. In a typical case each wafer would be connected at its ends across a p.d. of about 3 kV and there would be a difference of about 500 V between them. The space between the wafers also has a magnetic field of about 1,000 G whose vector is perpendicular both to the electric field and to the length of the silicon wafers.

A charged particle, or a photon, incident at the aperture on the left, in some such direction as that indicated in the diagram, liberates electrons from the surface of the silicon. These move through the crossed fields in a cycloidal arc and undergo acceleration, until they strike the surface of the same silicon wafer at a point further along its length. Further emission with multiplication now occurs, and the process is repeated in successive curved trajectories until the multiplied electron shower is gathered by the collector at the end. The number of multiplication stages can be varied, within limits, by adjusting the electric and magnetic fields. Gain up to $3 \times 10^6$ was reported with very low dark current and low noise.

The design features of interest are, firstly that the two wafers must be of reasonably uniform resistivity and very similar to each other in their electrical properties. Secondly, the resistance is an important factor; it must be high enough to give the necessary electric field, but low enough to pass sufficient bleeder current that local build-up of charge is prevented. This current is in the region of a few microamps. Silicon combines the necessary emission properties with suitable resistivity only if it is carefully doped and cooled to about 220° K. Some other semiconductor, perhaps gallium arsenide, might have the necessary properties at ambient temperatures. It is possible, too, that a material other than a semiconductor will be found suitable, and a leaky ceramic is under consideration.

The electron multipliers are used as detectors in mass spectrometry, where the necessary magnetic field can be provided by the fringing field of the spectrometer. For a given voltage gradient the device is not unduly sensitive to magnetic field; if the field strength increases there is an increase in the number of stages but the gain per stage is correspondingly reduced. It is therefore possible, over modest ranges, to sweep the spectrum past the detector by altering the spectrometer field. Twin multipliers have been made for simultaneous measurements on pairs of isotopes and there is a proposal for a multichannel assembly consisting of a number of wafers in a stack.

The necessity for cooling (which may be overcome in due course) is something of a drawback but it has the advantage that thermionic emission is then virtually zero and there is no dark current; the device will count reliably at 1 ion/sec. The rise time is about 1 nsec, depending on the length of the trajectory of the electrons between the slabs, and counting rates in excess of $10^6$/sec have been realized. The multiplier has been tested with $\alpha$-particles and will, presumably, respond

133

to any charged particle. It is suggested that a coating of $^{10}$B at the leading edge of the lower slab would convert it to a neutron detector.

## References

[1] WHITE, F. A., *Semiconductor Nuclear Particle Detectors*, Nat. Acad. Sci. (Washington), Publ. 871, p. 177

[2] WHITE, F. A., SHEFFIELD, J. C. and DAVIS, W. D., *Nucleonics* 19, No. 8 (1961) p. 58

# ELECTRONIC INSTRUMENTATION

## 9.1 Introduction

THE problems of pulse amplification, counting and analysis with semiconductor counters have much in common with those of any other detecting system depending on charge collection, and quite good results can be obtained without adopting any special techniques. Dearnaley and Whitehead[1] report an energy resolution of 20 keV for 5·4 MeV α-particles, using surface barrier counters and an A.E.R.E.-type 1430 amplifier, which is a conventional 2 Mc/s voltage amplifier with a 6 AK5 first stage. However, voltage amplification has drawbacks for use with barrier layer counters because the input varies with any change of bias, due to the change in input capacitance. Better results and higher stability are obtained by the use of charge-sensitive amplifiers, described later in this section. Although the methods described are designed primarily for use with barrier layer counters, they are largely applicable to bulk and to *P.I.N.* detectors.

## 9.2 Clipping Time and Rise Time

It is customary to use a detector and amplifier input circuit having a decay constant rather longer than the shortest coupling time constant used in the amplifier. The latter is therefore the clipping time constant, which determines the rate of pulse decay, and is denoted by the symbol '$\tau_a$' in this section. The quantity described earlier in this study as the 'collecting time', $t_c$, of a detector is the longest possible transit time for the slowest carriers and should, strictly, be termed the 'maximum collecting time'. In spectrometry the actual collecting times may vary with particle energy and, in any event, the shape of the pulse will do so. Therefore, to obtain strict linearity with energy, the clipping time should be considerably greater than the maximum collecting time. Ideally,

$$\tau_a > 5 \cdot t_c \qquad \qquad \ldots (9.1)$$

a condition which can often be met without difficulty. In some circumstances, for instance, with a high background count rate or when discriminating by adjustment of barrier depth (see Chapter 6.6), a clipping time constant substantially shorter than this may be used as the best compromise.

In spectrometry, where energy resolution is the prime requirement, it is customary to set the rise time constant of the amplifier equal to the clipping time constant, thus approximating to the condition of minimum amplifier noise. The rise time of the output pulse is then very much greater than $t_c$, and this arrangement is unsatisfactory if good time resolution is needed. For coincidence counting with a single amplifying system it is necessary to compromise, and the full capabilities of the detector are not realized. Arecchi et al.[2] discuss the problem of optimizing for resolving time and its effect on the signal-to-noise ratio. Dearnaley and Whitehead [3, 4] suggest a duplicated system, one part using fast amplification to provide good time resolution and to operate the gating circuit, and the other part being optimized for energy resolution.

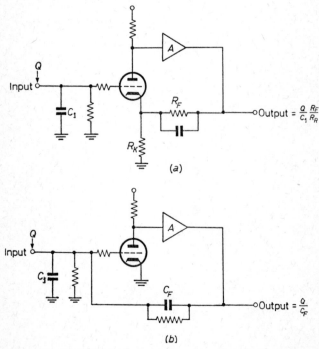

Figure 9.1. Pre-amplifier circuit configurations: (a) voltage-sensitive; (b) charge-sensitive

(E. Fairstein [6])

136

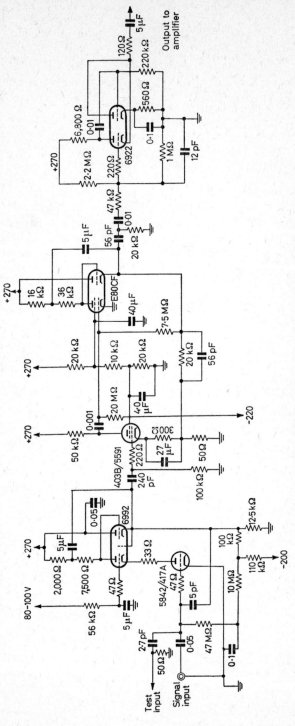

Figure 9.2. Circuit diagram of the Q-2069B-3 'Pre-amplifier for Solid State Detectors'

(J. L. Blankenship and C. J. Borkowski [9])

### 9.3 CHARGE-SENSITIVE AMPLIFIERS

A barrier layer counter has variable capacitance, and a voltage-sensitive amplifying system therefore gives output pulses of height dependent to some extent on the applied bias. To eliminate this effect pre-amplifiers are employed which are charge sensitive, and give pulse heights proportional to the charge released. They operate by employing negative charge feedback to the input capacitance. The basic difference in the circuit is illustrated[5] in *Figure 9.1*.

In both the circuits illustrated, $C_1$ is the input capacitance, which includes the variable capacitance of the detector. In circuit (b) the charge is, in effect, sucked off $C_1$ on to the constant capacitance, $C_F$. The complete circuit diagram of one type of charge-sensitive pre-amplifier is reproduced in *Figure 9.2* [6].

### 9.4 OPTIMIZATION FOR MINIMUM NOISE

Hansen and Goulding[7, 8] have investigated the problem of noise in the detector–amplifier system as a whole, basing their conclusions on experimental results with a guard-ring detector. They used charge-sensitive amplification with the rise time and clipping time constants equal, $\tau_a$.

With guard-ring counters the only apparent source of $1/f$ noise (see Chapter 2.9) is the 'tube flicker noise' arising in the amplifier input valve, and according to an empirical law the mean square noise level (most conveniently expressed in energy units) is given by

$$\text{Tube flicker noise} = 2 \times 10^{-4} C^2 \quad (\text{keV})^2 \quad \ldots (9.2)$$

In this expression, $C$ is the input capacitance in pF, which includes that of the detector, the input valve, strays and the integrating capacitor, $C_F$ of *Figure 9.1*. It should be noted that the effect of flicker noise is independent of the amplifier time constant, $\tau_a$. This is a consequence of the fact that the gain of an amplifier having equal time constants is frequency-dependent and is given by a relationship of the form

$$G = G_0 \frac{(2\pi f \tau_a)}{1 + (2\pi f \tau_a)^2} \quad \ldots (9.3)$$

It follows from this that the band width is proportional to the low frequency cut-off. Tube flicker noise, and any other noise source having a $1/f$ dependence results, therefore, in a noise component independent of $\tau_a$.

With guard-ring detectors flicker noise is negligible compared with other sources of noise. With other detectors this may not be the case, but eqn. (9.2) shows that the effect cannot be altered by adjustment of $\tau_a$ and the optimization of the amplifier time constant, described below, would not be affected.

Hansen and Goulding, with their guard-ring counters, found only two sources of noise which were really significant. These are described as 'tube shot noise' and 'detector leakage noise' and their contributions to the variance in the output pulse are given by the equations:

Tube shot noise $= 2 \times 10^{-2} C^2/g_m \tau_a \quad \text{(keV)}^2 \quad \ldots (9.4)$

Detector leakage noise $= 1 \cdot 6 \times 10^{-1} i_L \tau_a \quad \text{(keV)}^2 \quad \ldots (9.5)$

where

$C =$ the total input capacitance in pF ($\sim 80$)

$g_m =$ the input tube mutual conductance in mA/V ($\sim 16$)

$i_L =$ detector dark current in m$\mu$A ($\sim 50$)

$\tau_a =$ the amplifier time constants in $\mu$sec ($\sim 1$)

Detector leakage noise is of the same nature as 'current noise', described in Chapter 2.9. It is clear from eqns. (9.4) and (9.5) that the input capacitance and the dark current should be kept as low as possible. When this has been done there is an optimum value of $\tau_a$ which will give the lowest combined noise level. This is

$$\tau_{\text{opt}} = 0 \cdot 35 \, C/(g_m i_L)^{\frac{1}{2}} \quad \mu\text{sec} \qquad \ldots (9.6)$$

and the resulting noise level is

$$\overline{\text{noise}^2} = 0 \cdot 11 \, C(i_L/g_m)^{\frac{1}{2}} \quad \text{(keV)}^2 \qquad \ldots (9.7)$$

This is the variance, to convert to the normal measure for energy resolution,

$$2 \cdot 36 \times \overline{\text{noise}} \, (\text{standard deviation}) = \overline{\text{noise}} \, (\text{f.w.h.m.})$$

As an example, if $g_m = 16$, $i_L = 50$ and $C = 80$, then $\tau_{\text{opt}}$ is 1 $\mu$sec and $\overline{\text{noise}} = 9 \cdot 2$ keV (f.w.h.m.). It is mentioned in Chapter 6.3 that, for 5 MeV particles, statistical fluctuations are equivalent to 10 keV (f.w.h.m.). Squaring and adding these two figures and taking the square root, gives the figure 13·4 keV (f.w.h.m.) as the energy resolution which could be achieved with these parameters. It is of interest to compare these figures with the very good experimental result (15 keV for 5·8 MeV $\alpha$-particles) analysed in Chapter 6.3.

Hansen and Goulding continued their study on the assumption that $i_L$, for a barrier layer counter, could be calculated using a relationship of the form of eqn. (4.11$a$) (for a $P$–$N$ counter),

$$i_L = \frac{38(\rho V)^{\frac{1}{2}}}{\tau_0} \quad m\mu A/cm^2 \qquad \ldots (9.8)$$

In this case, however, $\tau_0$ is *not* the actual carrier lifetime of the parent crystal; it is termed the 'effective carrier lifetime' and is treated as a parameter, chosen to give the best fit to the actual curve of reverse current/voltage. With guard-ring counters the reverse currents do follow, very closely, a law such as this for moderate bias volts. Other barrier layer counters differ among themselves but in many cases eqn. (9.8) would apply roughly over most of the practical range of operation.

Using eqn. (9.8) it can be shown that there is now an optimum bias,

$$V_{opt} = \frac{9 \times 10^8 A^2}{\rho C_1^2} \quad V \qquad \ldots (9.9)$$

where $A$ is the detector area in $cm^2$, $\rho$ is in $\Omega cm$ and $C_1$ is the input capacitance, excluding that of the barrier layer, in pF. The resulting noise level is

$$\overline{noise^2} = 250(C_1/\tau_0 g_m)^{\frac{1}{2}} \quad (keV)^2 \qquad \ldots (9.10)$$

If, for example, $A = 0.8$, $\rho = 1,500$, $\tau_0 = 500$ ($\mu sec$), $g_m = 16$ and $C_1 = 25$, then,

$$V_{opt} = 615 \text{ V (counter capacitance} = 35 \text{ pF)}$$

$$\tau_{opt} = 0.62 \text{ } \mu sec$$

$$\overline{noise^2} = 11.4 \text{ } (keV)^2$$

Hansen and Goulding found very close agreement between the theory described above and the actual noise levels obtained with guard-ring counters. The very high value for $V_{opt}$ in the above example is of great interest because a narrow view of the noise problem (considering the detector only) leads to the conclusion that bias should be kept fairly low.

From eqn. (4.9a), the collecting time in this counter (a $P$–$N$ type) would be about 7 nsec and the optimum amplifier constant for minimum noise easily satisfies eqn. (9.1). This would be the case under normal circumstances but if the reverse current were exceptionally large, as, for example, in the case of a $dE/dx$ counter, it may be necessary to use a value for $\tau_a$ larger than the optimum for noise. In bulk counters and *P.I.N.* detectors, where $t_c$ is much longer, it would not usually be possible to optimize $\tau_a$ on noise. Even with barrier layer counters other considerations may often be dominant. In the example given above, a bias of 615 V might well exceed the breakdown level.

## 9.5 OTHER SPECIAL REQUIREMENTS

Although acceptable results can be obtained with quite ordinary electronics, realization of the full capabilities of semiconductor detectors requires a certain amount of specialized design, of which the charge sensitive amplifier and optimization for minimum noise are only two examples. Under the best conditions with a good counter the noise level of the amplifier will usually be the limiting factor on energy resolution, even after optimization. Low noise is therefore a requirement justifying special efforts in electronic design. Another requirement is extraordinarily good stability, and in this respect charge sensitive amplifiers are superior.

Although it is possible in favourable circumstances to realize almost all the energy resolution of which the detector is theoretically capable, this still fails to meet many experimental requirements because it is often necessary to employ coincidence, or anti-coincidence counting. As already noted in section 2, the optimum system for energy resolution is incompatible with good time resolution and the remedy of employing two separate amplifying systems (section 2) coupled in parallel is an expensive expedient. Moreover, it still leaves something to be desired, because optimization should really start with the detector and the input circuit. There is, therefore an unsatisfied requirement for a single amplifying system which will combine good time resolution with good energy resolution.

When the detector capacitance is very high, the tube shot noise becomes very large [see eqn. (9.4)]. It is then no longer feasible to optimize for minimum noise and a transistor amplifier gives superior signal-to-noise ratio.

## REFERENCES

[1] DEARNALEY, G. and WHITEHEAD, A. B., *A.E.R.E. Rep.* R-3437 (1960)
[2] ARECCHI, F. T., CAVALLERI, G., GATTI, E. and SVELTO, V., *Semiconductor Nuclear Particle Detectors*, Nat. Acad. Sci. (Washington), Publ. 871, p. 226
[3] DEARNALEY, G. and WHITEHEAD, A. B., *A.E.R.E. Rep.* R-3662 (1961)
[4] DEARNALEY, G., FERGUSON, A. T. G., WHITEHEAD, A. B. and MONTAGUE, J., *Proceedings of a conference on Nuclear Electronics* (May 1961), I.A.E.A.

[5] FAIRSTEIN, E., *Solid State Radiation Detectors*, Inst. Radio Engrs, N.Y., N.S.8, No. 1 (Jan. 1961) p. 129

[6] BLANKENSHIP, J. L. and BORKOWSKI, C. J., *ibid.* p. 17

[7] HANSEN, W. and GOULDING, F. S., *Semiconductor Nuclear Particle Detectors*, Nat. Acad. Sci. (Washington), Publ. 871, p. 202

[8] HANSEN, W. and GOULDING, F. S., *Proceedings of a Conference on Nuclear Electronics* (May 1961), I.A.E.A.

# 10

# FURTHER DEVELOPMENTS

## 10.1 INTRODUCTION

WHILE this book was under preparation for the press the rapid development of new techniques and discovery continued with unabated vigour. It was found impracticable to revise each section without causing undue delay in publication and the deficiency has therefore been remedied by the late addition of this chapter, which describes the more important aspects of recent work.

## 10.2 OHMIC CONTACTS

A rather naive consideration of the properties of metals and semiconductors would lead to the conclusion that the nature of any contact between the two ought to be governed by the relative positions of the Fermi level, and that it should be easily possible to make good ohmic contacts. *Figure 10.1* illustrates this type of argument for the case of an $N$-type semiconductor and a metal when the Fermi level in the latter is initially higher than in the semiconductor. This last statement is equivalent to saying that the metal has a smaller work function.

In *Figure 10.1*, diagram $(a)$ shows the relative positions, on an energy scale, of the Fermi levels in the two materials when they are not in contact. When a junction is made between them there is at first an excess flow of electrons from the metal into the semiconductor, where lower unoccupied energy levels are available in the conduction band. The metal therefore acquires a positive charge in comparison with the semiconductor and the energy levels therein are lowered accordingly (see Chapter 3.1). The equilibrium condition to be expected is shown in *Figure 10.1(b)*, where the Fermi levels coincide and there is a potential difference, $Q$, across the junction. If $W_m$ and $W_s$ are the respective work functions, then

$$eQ = W_s - W_m$$

The downward curvature of the boundaries of the energy gap can

143

readily be understood as a consequence of the potential difference; electrons near the bottom of the conduction band, but physically close to the junction, must be in a relatively low energy state because of the proximity of the positive charge in the metal. Similarly, a hole at the top of the valence band, somewhere in the body of the semiconductor, would have to acquire additional energy in order to approach the junction.

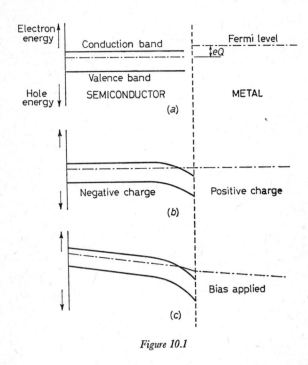

*Figure 10.1*

If the difference in work functions is large enough, the lower boundary of the conduction band should fall below the Fermi level in the vicinity of the junction. If, now, a bias is applied in such a sense as to increase the inherent p.d. across the junction (i.e. reverse bias) the condition illustrated in diagram (*c*) is to be expected. The majority carriers are able to flow from left to right across the junction without encountering any barrier, the applied potential difference is, therefore, not concentrated at the junction but is distributed through the body of the materials, as shown by the general slope of the Fermi level. Such a junction would be an excellent ohmic contact. Moreover, it is seen from diagram (c) that a barrier does exist to oppose the flow of holes which would otherwise traverse the junction from the metal into the semiconductor. Since holes are the minority carriers this fact does not appreciably affect the conductivity across the junction, but it does mean that such a contact would be 'non-injecting' as far as holes are concerned. A bias applied in the opposite sense yields virtually the same result; there is still no appreciable barrier for electrons but there *is* a barrier, though somewhat less effective, for holes.

This simple theory can readily be extended to the case of contacts between a $P$-type semiconductor and metals but it will not be pursued any further here, except to point out that the argument is facilitated if the Fermi level in the metal is now regarded as the lower boundary of a zone of energy levels occupied by holes. The conclusion is reached that good ohmic contacts ought to exist if (a) the semiconductor is $N$-type and $W_m < W_s$; (b) the semiconductor is $P$-type and $W_m > W_s$.

It is doubtful if the above ideas have any real validity in practice because, as already described in earlier sections, there is invariably some surface effect. As stated in Chapter 5.2, there is usually an oxide layer. If special steps are taken to eliminate this there will be a surface layer of semiconductor contaminated with the applied metal, and this then controls the properties of the junction. Because of these boundary effects it is rather difficult to make good ohmic, non-injecting contacts, which explains the use of deep diffusion for bulk counters (see Chapter 2.2), where a really good result is essential. Gold appears to be reasonably successful for connexions to $P$-type material, but until recently no very satisfactory method for $N$-type materials had been found.

Andrews[1] succeeded in resolving this problem for $N$-type silicon by trying various metals of lower work function. He found that coatings of aluminium, beryllium or magnesium applied by vaporization *in vacuo* appear to behave in accordance with the ideas described above and illustrated in *Figure 10.1*. It is not suggested that conditions at the junction in practical cases are actually the same as implied by *Figure 10.1*—they are almost certainly more complicated—but the result is an ohmic, non-injecting contact. Andrews found it unnecessary to take any special steps to eliminate the oxide layer and suggests that some chemical action is probably involved. The complexity of this subject is illustrated by the fact that aluminium will also make a good ohmic contact to $P$-type silicon, but in this case an alloyed junction is necessary (see Chapter 2.6).

Ohmic contacts of this type are now being generally used for the back contacts of surface barrier detectors. In particular, Dearnaley now employs an aluminium coating in place of the silver paste mentioned in Chapter 5.3 (private communication).

## 10.3  THIN DETECTORS

Considerable improvements are reported in the techniques for making thin detectors. Andrews[1] exploited the advantages of his non-injecting back contacts, described in the previous section, to obtain lower reverse currents and reduced noise. With all barrier layer counters the bias applied is such that any excess minority carriers appearing in the base crystal behind the junction will tend to increase the reverse current. If the counter is reasonably thick any such minority carriers created or injected at the back contact will move slowly towards the junction and will not survive long enough to reach it. In a thin counter, particularly if the depletion zone extends right through the crystal, this does not apply and the use of a non-injecting back contact is very important.

The back contact of a surface barrier, $N$–$P$ detector is biased in the same sense as that illustrated in *Figure 10.1(c)*, and the new contact therefore provides a most effective barrier against the injection of holes. It should be noted, also, that as windowless performance at both sides is a primary object, a contact made by deep diffusion would be unacceptable. Andrews made detectors ranging in thickness from 0·05 to 0·1 mm thick in 2,000 $\Omega$cm $N$-type silicon with a gold front face and a back contact of aluminium. A bias of 5 V gave full depletion with a reverse current of only 0·2 μA at 24° C; the resolution was 0·7 per cent on 5 MeV $\alpha$-particles. With the bias increased to 12 V the reverse current was 0·4 μA. This result should be compared with that obtained by Wegner when using $P$–$N$ counters, described in Chapter 6.7. Furthermore, Andrews reports that the noise level was less, in proportion to the reverse current, than with other types of contact, and that useful performance was obtained with reverse currents of several microamps.

An improved technique for lapping and finishing thin detectors is described by Innskeep[2]. After grinding and etching in the ordinary way down to a thickness of about 0·2 mm, the wafer is mounted on a microscope cover glass, using a thin layer of wax. With this backing further lapping can be done without fractures and final processing is completed without removing the wafer from the glass. Access to the other face of the wafer is obtained by etching a window through the glass, using hydrofluoric acid, and the detector is mounted with its annular glass support. Counters down to about 0·05 mm in thickness with an aperture 9·5 mm in diameter have been made in this way, and it is thought probable that the thickness could be further reduced to about 0·02 mm. Exceptionally good uniformity of thickness is claimed for the method.

## 10.4 WINDOWS

The existence of a small but finite window, even on the best diffused junction detectors, appears to be confirmed in a report by Williams and Webb[3]. Measurements were made by careful experiments with α-particles entering obliquely at various angles of incidence. It was found that the window thickness is very close to one-half the phosphorus diffusion depth. The authors of this report conclude that the window is due, as expected, to a surface layer in which hole lifetime is too short to allow collection by diffusion, and they further conclude that it is associated with impurity concentrations exceeding $5 \times 10^{18}/cm^3$. By doping with arsenic, in place of phosphorus, they showed that if the surface concentration is kept below this figure the window thickness is much reduced.

Diffused junction counters made with phosphorus have surface impurity concentrations of the order $10^{21}$ atoms/cm$^2$ and have windows not less than 0·1 μ thick, equal to 0·025 mg/cm$^2$. This would result in carrier losses equivalent to about 15 keV, for a 5 MeV α-particle. It was found that gaseous diffusion is superior to paint-on methods (a conclusion also reached by Innskeep[2]) and that the latter gives diffusion depths greater than expected.

## 10.5 DETECTORS WITH HIGH BIAS

Fox has continued his development of techniques for preventing breakdown (previously mentioned by Blankenship[4]) and in conjunction with Borkowski has achieved startling results[5]. Working with silicon surface barrier counters mounted in ceramic rings (*Figure 10.2*), they concluded that the surface of the silicon in contact with epoxy resin used to seal the edge of the wafer was much more $N$-type than the bulk of the crystal. In consequence of this, it may be expected that there is a high surface concentration of positive charge, arising from ionized donors. Since the active gold surface is negatively biased, it follows that a high electric field exists round the edge of the active front face, at P in *Figure 10.2*. It was observed that breakdown usually occurs in this region.

The surface condition of silicon when in contact with various materials was investigated and it was found that a $P$-type surface could be induced by adding iodine to the epoxy resin and using an amine-free hardener. The composition was, Ciba No. CN 502 epoxy plus 1 per cent iodine, mixed 5:1 with Epoxylite No. 204-B hardener. A number of counters were made with a fillet of this resin applied round the edge of the active surface, as shown in *Figure 10.3*. The junction is still at P but the edge of the gold film is removed to $Q$, away from the junction field.

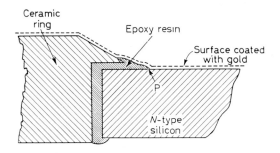

Ceramic ring

Epoxy resin

Surface coated with gold

P

N-type silicon

*Figure 10.2*

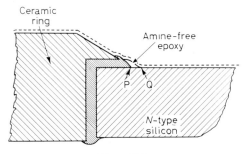

Ceramic ring

Amine-free epoxy

P   Q

N-type silicon

*Figure 10.3*

Using 6,000 Ω silicon, counters were made by this method, capable of supporting a bias more than 4,000 V. This is double the highest figure previously reported (also due to Fox).

Such counters, however, were found to give excessive noise at bias volts exceeding 1,000 and it was found necessary to resort to a guard-ring structure, as shown in the photograph (*Figure 10.4*). The noise generated at the junction edge is thereby isolated from the counter circuit. Emphasis is placed on the need to keep the resistivity of the guard-ring gap very high and a figure of $6 \times 10^{10}$ Ω/sq. is quoted. For this, the surface concerned must be $N$-type and must remain so; ambient atmospheres which cause inversion reduce the resistivity drastically. Fox and Borkowski[5] do not explain how inversion is

*Figure 10.4*
(R. J. Fox and C. J. Borkowski [5], by courtesy of the Inst. Radio Engrs, New York)

prevented, in view of the fact that air is one of the ambients concerned, but it may perhaps be assumed that the normal thin layer due to oxide is acceptable.

The method of attaching the central contact, just visible in *Figure 10.4*, is of interest. After mounting the etched silicon in the ceramic ring, the end of a gold wire 0·002 in. in diameter is beaded in a flame and secured to the centre with a small drop of amine-free epoxy resin. The wire itself must not touch the surface of the silicon. The necessary electrical contact is then made when the surface layer

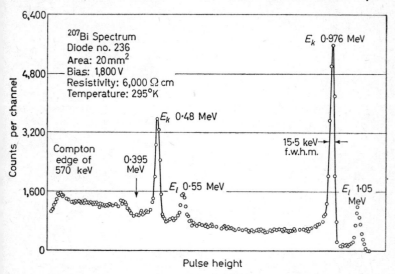

*Figure 10.5. Conversion electron spectrum of $^{207}$Bi taken at 1,800 V bias with a guard-ring surface barrier detector*

(R. J. Fox and C. J. Borkowski [5], by courtesy of the Inst. Radio Engrs, New York).

of gold is deposited by vaporization *in vacuo*. The back contact of these detectors was made by vaporization of gold on to a lapped surface; it is possible that further improvement would be obtained by using aluminium in place of gold.

These counters gave excellent results with electrons; *Figure 10.5* shows the spectrum of the conversion electrons from $^{207}$Bi, obtained in air at room temperature with a depletion zone of depth about 1·5 mm. *Figure 10.6* shows even better energy resolution on the upper part of this same spectrum, obtained by slight cooling to 273° K and with a slightly reduced bias. The resolution (f.w.h.m.) on the $K$ peak is better than 1 per cent, which is a very considerable improvement on previous results. It may be noted that the results depicted in *Figures*

*10.5* and *10.6* were both obtained with barrier depths rather less than the end point range of the most energetic electrons concerned (a 1

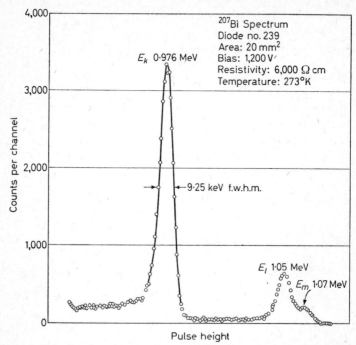

*Figure 10.6. Expanded spectrum of the conversion electrons from the 1·06 MeV transition of* $^{207}$Bi *taken at 1,200 V and 273° K with a guard-ring surface barrier detector*
(R. J. Fox and C. J. Borkowski [5], by courtesy of the Inst. Radio Engrs, New York)

MeV electron has an end point of about 2 mm in silicon). It is probable that any loss of resolution arising from this fact is compensated for by the reduced noise associated with minimum bias.

## 10.6   LITHIUM ION DRIFT

The production of *P.I.N.* detectors by this method, first suggested by Pell[6, 7] and followed up by Mayer[8], has excited considerable interest and they are now being made by many groups with constantly improving techniques. A variant of special interest is reported by Blankenship and Borkowski[9], who describe a technique whereby the thick dead layer on the *N* face may be considerably reduced; at the same time, the uniformity of the surface is improved and energy resolution benefits.

This account must begin with an explanation of the reason why counters made by the method described in Chapter 7.2 do have very thick dead layers. The trouble is that the surface concentration obtainable in diffusing lithium is considerably lower than that obtainable with phosphorus, and this sets an upper limit to the conductivity obtainable in the surface layers. In order to obtain a sufficiently low sheet resistance to make a good diode it is, therefore, necessary to have a much deeper junction than is the case with phosphorus or boron. Furthermore, an adequate junction depth must remain even after the drift process. The dead layer is usually 100 $\mu$ or more.

Further difficulties arise in connexion with low surface conductivity because it is not easy to make a good ohmic contact, and it is reported[9] that the spectra of charged particles show distortions due to unknown phenomena related to the contact. It is of interest that photon spectra do not show this effect.

Another problem arises from the considerable chemical activity and volatility of lithium. It may be applied as a suspension in oil or by vacuum vaporization. In either case, an excess must be used to allow for losses during diffusion: by reaction with air if exposed to the atmosphere or by evaporation otherwise. The excess may be removed by washing in water or alcohol, but the surface of the doped silicon is usually damaged.

In the method of Blankenship and Borkowski the first step after etching is to carry out a phosphorus diffusion on the $N$ face, to a depth of about 2 $\mu$. This remains undisturbed throughout the subsequent processing and provides the low sheet resistance needed, so that the surface concentration of the lithium subsequently diffused is no longer of prime importance. The next step is to form the back contact (in this case of aluminium) and then follows the vacuum vaporization of a thin, carefully controlled layer of lithium and, on top of this, a layer 200–400 $\mu g/cm^2$ of aluminium. The lithium applied is only a little more than is needed to compensate the desired thickness of the base crystal; the aluminium is a temporary covering, to prevent loss of the lithium by chemical action or evaporation.

Diffusion is carried out at 400°C for 10 min in argon, which diffuses all the lithium into the silicon. The aluminium, which is not alloyed, is easily removed leaving a clean undamaged surface which is not highly chemically active.

The method of ion drift described in the report also has a novel feature, which enables the drift rate to be kept to a higher level throughout. The field in the intrinsic zone of the crystal during drift is uniform and approximately equal to $V/W$ (see Chapter 7.3). The drift rate may be defined as the rate of increase of $W$, and this is clearly equal to the speed of the ions. Therefore

$$\frac{\mathrm{d}w}{\mathrm{d}t} = \text{drift rate} = \frac{V}{W}\mu$$

It has been common practice in the past to couple the diode thermally to some form of heat sink (for example, a copper block with the diode pressed against it) maintained at a constant temperature, and to drift with a constant bias throughout. Under these conditions the temperature within the crystal really depends on the power dissipated, and therefore rises as the process continues, due to the increase in the reverse current. The temperature of the heat sink and the bias applied are therefore limited by the conditions at the end of the process, when thermal runaway is most likely due to the high reverse current.

Blankenship and Borkowski employed a servo system to control the temperature of their heat sink. Constant bias was still used, but the heat sink temperature was adjusted throughout so as to maintain a constant power dissipation. The servo system had a time constant less than 30 sec. Since the reverse current depends strongly on temperature, the method of control based on power dissipated is more effective in preventing thermal runaway. It was possible to run at a power level of 50 W with a diode of area 0·5 cm$^2$.

These counters, made with a preliminary phosphorus diffusion and only a limited amount of lithium could be drifted to reduce the dead layer to about 10 µ or less. This, and the improved electrical contact at the surface, gave substantially better energy resolution. They were tried out on the conversion electrons from $^{207}$Bi and spectra almost identical with *Figures 10.5* and *10.6* are published. The detectors concerned were made from silicon of resistivity 50–100 Ω cm and had an aperture of 25 mm$^2$. The first spectrum (similar to *Figure 10.5*) was obtained at room temperature with a bias of 50 V; the intrinsic layer was ≥ 1·65 mm.

The authors of this report describe the counters as '$P^+$—$I$—$N^+$ diode detectors'. The positive signs indicate that the layers concerned are heavily doped. Using the same nomenclature an ordinary diffused junction counter would be described as '$P^+$—$P$—$N^+$'.

## 10.7   TIME RESOLUTION

The factors affecting the recorded pulse rise time are

   (*a*)  the collecting time,
   (*b*)  the time constants of the detector and amplifier input circuits,
   (*c*)  the rise time of the amplifier.

In earlier chapters the first of these factors has been considered at some length and the third has at least been mentioned, but little has been said about the second. As this is very much a detector problem, some effort is made here to repair the omission.

It is pointed out by Raymo and Mayer[10] and elsewhere in the literature that the appearance of charge at the boundaries of the depletion zone does not complete the process of signalling the entry of the particle. The charge must pass through the series resistance due to the bulk of the crystal, behind the depletion zone, and also the front and back contacts before reaching the amplifier input. These resistances are denoted by the resister $R_s$ in the impedance diagram of *Figure 4.1*, Chapter 4.2. Reduced to essentials, this is a case of a charge

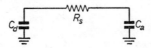

*Figure 10.7*

being placed on a capacitor, $C_d$, of *Figure 10.7* and then being shared between that capacitor and the amplifier input capacitance, $C_a$. The time constant is

$$\frac{R_s.C_d.C_a}{C_d+C_a}$$

Consider a fairly typical case of voltage amplification using a counter of aperture 20 mm$^2$ made from 6,000 $\Omega$ cm $P$-type silicon with an undepleted zone 1 mm thick: ignoring contact resistance, $R_s$ would be 3,000 $\Omega$. With a bias of 20 V the counter capacitance would be about 60 pF and a reasonable figure for $C_a$ would be 20 pF. The time constant would be at least 45 nsec. This detector would give complete carrier collection in 30 nsec, so the pulse rise time at the amplifier would not depend at all on the properties of the barrier region and the system would not realize full time resolution.

The obvious remedy is to keep the series resistance down to a minimum, by using a counter only slightly thicker than the depletion zone and by employing good contacts. The non-injecting back contact described in section 2 is clearly helpful, and where time resolution is all important thin detectors with full depletion zones offer a decided advantage.

To indicate the importance of these factors, it is instructive to pursue the example a little further. Very approximately, the 10 per cent to 90 per cent rise time of the detector considered above would be 8 nsec, and the time constant should certainly not exceed this. The series resistance should therefore be reduced to about 500 $\Omega$, and the undepleted layer would have to be less than 150 $\mu$, even with the best of contacts.

Charge sensitive amplifiers, although superior in flexibility and in some other respects, are not suitable if time resolution is important. Referring to *Figure 9.1*, Chapter 9.3, the negative feedback has the effect of keeping the grid potential virtually constant, so that the input capacitance is very large. It is, in fact equal to $C_F(G+1)$, where $G$ is the amplifier gain. The time constant of the detector and input circuit is therefore very nearly $R_s.C_d$, and this is usually larger than for voltage amplification. The detector considered above, with 1 mm of un-depleted crystal, would give an input time constant of 180 nsec.

It may be noted here that the resistance of the undepleted layer and the carrier collecting time are both proportional to the resistivity of the parent crystal, so this problem is much the same for detectors made from crystal of any resistivity. Finally, as noted in Chapter 9.2, if full time resolution is to be achieved, the rise time of the amplifier should also be less than the carrier collecting time. At present this, and the capabilities of the analysing or coincidence circuits, are often the limiting factors.

## 10.8   MISCELLANEOUS NOTES

It seems appropriate to mention a few other matters which are not explained here in detail but references are quoted where available.

Dearnaley et al.[11, 12] give a more detailed description of their work on neutron detection, including a theoretical assessment of the various methods. They conclude that proton recoil (see Chapter 6.8) is basically the most efficient for flux monitoring but, of course, will not yield a spectrum. The $^3He(n,p)$ $^3H$ reaction, also mentioned in Chapter 6.8, is the best prospect for spectrometry. The counters and their performance are described in considerable detail.

The properties of barrier layer counters as photocells were investigated by Tuzzolino et al.[13] They found that with suitable low noise amplification a barrier layer counter could be used with a scintillator and would give results only marginally inferior to those obtained with a photomultiplier. The possibilities for instrumentation in space, using miniaturized transistor electronics, are pointed out.

Two aspects of charge collection are discussed in great detail by Tove and Falk[14] and Miller and Gibson[15]. The first deals with the carrier transit time in both forms of barrier layer counter and the build-up of charge on the boundaries of the barrier layer is worked out in detail. The second analyses the processes contributing to carrier losses, with particular reference to the pulse height defect in detecting fission fragments. It is concluded that the defect is not due to a dead layer. Recombination on impurity centres in the dense plasma appears to be the prime factor.

The phenomenon of multiple peaking does not seem to have been explained very satisfactorily. The usual idea, that it is due to in-homogeneities is particularly difficult to accept as an explanation of multiple peaking when it appears only as a consequence of radiation damage, in a detector which was formerly good. This, and other aspects of radiation damage in barrier layer counters is the subject of a paper by E. M. Gunnersen, to be published in the near future.

It has already been mentioned (Chapter 9.5) that semiconductor counters require rather special amplifiers if their full potentialities are to be realized, but this is not the only aspect of their employment which calls for new developments in electronics. Dearnaley[16] points out that pulse height analysis of a spectrum of width 5 MeV with a detector of energy resolution 20 keV (f.w.h.m.) calls for at least 500 to 1,000 channels, and that in some circumstances a stability of 0·1 per cent may be required over long periods and for fluctuating counting speeds. Experimentation in nuclear physics generally is undergoing a revolution in automation by electronics and the special needs of semiconductor counters are rapidly being catered for. For example, particle discrimination using $dE/dx$, $E$ detection requires fast mul-tiplication of the signals obtained; one solution is described by Vincent and Kaine[17].

However, the subject of electronic data handling is outside the scope of this work. The interested reader will find a number of papers on those aspects of the subject which are particularly relevant to semiconductor counters in the publications of the Institution of Radio Engineers mentioned in the table of references, and also in the Proceedings of the I.A.E.A. Conference in Belgrade.

## REFERENCES

[1] ANDREWS, P. T., *Proceedings of the Symposium on Nuclear Instruments*, Harwell, 1961 (Ed. by J. B. Birks), Heywood (1962)

[2] INSKEEP, C. N., *Proceedings of the Eighth Scintillation Counter Symposium*, Inst. Radio Engrs, N.Y., N.S.9, No. 3 (June 1962) p. 167

[3] WILLIAMS, R. L. and WEBB, P. P., *ibid.* p. 160

[4] BLANKENSHIP, J. L., *Semiconductor Nuclear Particle Detectors*, Nat. Acad. Sci. (Washington), Publ. 871, p. 43

[5] FOX, R. J. and BORKOWSKI, C. J., *Proceedings of the Eighth Scintillation Counter Symposium*, Inst. Radio Engrs, N.Y., N.S.9, No. 3 (June 1962) p. 213

[6] PELL, E. M., *J. appl. Phys.* 31 (1960) 291

[7] PELL, E. M., *Semiconductor Nuclear Particle Detectors*, Nat. Acad. Sci. (Washington), Publ. 871, p. 136

[8] MAYER, J. W., BAILY, N. A. and DUNLAP, H. L., *Proceedings of a Conference on Nuclear Electronics* (May 1961), I.A.E.A.

[9] BLANKENSHIP, J. L. and BORKOWSKI, C. J., *Proceedings of the Eighth Scintillation Counter Symposium*, Inst. Radio Engrs, N.Y., N.S.9, No. 3 (June 1962) p. 181

[10] RAYMO, C. T. and MAYER, J. W., *Solid State Radiation Detectors*, Inst. Radio Engrs, N.Y., N.S.8, No. 1 (Jan. 1961) p. 157

[11] DEARNALEY, G,. FERGUSON, A. T. G. and MORRISON, C. C., *Proceedings of the Eighth Scintillation Counter Symposium*, Inst. Radio Engrs, N.Y., N.S.9, No. 3 (June 1962) p. 174

[12] DEARNALEY, G. and FERGUSON, A. T. G., *Proceedings of the Symposium on Nuclear Instruments*, Harwell, 1961 (Ed. by J. B. Birks), Heywood (1962)

[13] TUZZOLINO, A. J., HUBBARD, E. L., PERKINS, M. A. and FAN, C. Y., *J. appl. Phys.* 33 (1962) 148

[14] TOVE, P. A. and FALK, K., *Nuclear Inst.* 12, No. 2 (1961) p. 278

[15] MILLER, G. L. and GIBSON, W. M., *Proceedings of a Conference on Nuclear Electronics* (May 1961), I.A.E.A.

[16] DEARNALEY, G., *A.E.R.E. Rep.* R-3874 (1961)

[17] VINCENT, C. H. and KAINE, D., *Fast Pulse Multiplication by Logarithmic Attenuators* (to be published)

# 11

## CONCLUDING REMARKS

BECAUSE of the great advantages to be derived from having detectors designed specifically to suit particular applications, a number of laboratories have installed their own equipment for making and testing them. It is unfortunate, that with existing supplies of silicon the manufacture (whether in the laboratory or on a commercial scale) of detectors is something of a hit and miss venture. Improvements in this respect can be confidently anticipated, but in the meantime it is not enough to design and make one detector for one purpose; a number have to be made and the best selected.

There is no reason whatever to believe that the various types of particle detector described, and the techniques for making them, represent all the major possibilities. On the contrary, it is to be expected that further variants will be discovered, each with its own particular merits and applications, and it seems probable that in a few years time they will be very widely used to replace gaseous counters and scintillation detectors, at least for particle spectrometry. For gamma and beta detection semiconductor methods still leave much to be desired, largely because of the difficulty in obtaining an adequate sensitive volume. Their possibilities in this respect are considered by Jones[1], where the rather small signal is also noted as a disadvantage. Further development of bulk detectors, or ion drift techniques, may overcome the volume problem and the integral transistor may improve the signal size. Alternatively, some entirely different approach may be found.

The possibility of using radiation effects to condition semiconductor crystals is attractive. Apart from the possibilities of general irradiation to obtain uniform increase in resistivity by compensation, it may be feasible to obtain accurate layer effects. For example, ionic bombardment might be employed to obtain surface inversion layers of greater uniformity than those obtainable by diffusion. This would have the further advantage of avoiding heat treatment. A preliminary investigation of one technique for radiation surface doping is reported by Rourke et al.[2]

The effects of low temperatures on semiconductor counters have been discussed where relevant, but nothing has been said about operation at high temperatures. There is no immediate prospect of obtaining good semiconductor detection at temperatures much in excess of 100° C. Any progress there may be in this direction must await further developments in the purification of materials with a large energy gap. Silicon carbide, $E_G = 3 \cdot 0$ eV, or zinc oxide, $E_G = 3 \cdot 2$ eV, are perhaps the most hopeful prospects.

It is hoped that the references made will be found adequate as a 'lead in' for the more detailed study of any particular aspect. For general reading, to tie up the loose ends or to clarify matters not adequately explained here, the report on the conference at Asheville[3] is recommended, which contains a long bibliography. The introduction to semiconductor physics in Chapters 1 and 3 is intended only to give a background good enough for a reasonable understanding of particle detectors. It is hardly adequate for the more serious student, who is advised to extend his reading of this subject. A number of suitable books are available some of which are mentioned in the references, but it should be remembered that these are written with a view to other applications and are apt to be deficient, or even a little misleading, in some respects. For example, the subject of trapping and its effects is generally inadequately dealt with and the same applies to the physics of deep depletion layers and reverse currents. A study of the original papers is the best approach for these subjects.

REFERENCES

[1] JONES, A. R., *Nucleonics* 18, 10 (1960) p. 86
[2] ROURKE, F. M., SHEFFIELD, J. C. and WHITE, F. A., *Rev. sci. Instrum.* 32, 4 (1961) 455
[3] *Semiconductor Nuclear Particle Detectors*, Nat. Acad. Sci. (Washington), Publ. 871

# APPENDIX A

THE expressions derived from theory for barrier layers, ion drift intrinsic layers and reverse current are correct in electrostatic units. The conversion to practical units is an irritating exercise. A list of conversion factors is given below, together with some useful constants.

CONVERSION FACTORS

| Electrostatic unit of: | Practical unit | Ratio of practical to e.s.u |
|---|---|---|
| e.m.f. | V | $3·33 \times 10^{-3}$ |
| Charge | C | $3 \times 10^{9}$ |
| Current | A | $3 \times 10^{9}$ |
| Resistance | $\Omega$ | $1·11 \times 10^{-12}$ |
| Resistivity | $\Omega$ cm | $1·11 \times 10^{-12}$ |
| Capacitance | F | $9 \times 10^{-11}$ |

CONSTANTS

The electronic charge, $q = 1·6 \times 10^{-19}$ C
$\phantom{The electronic charge, q} = 4·8 \times 10^{-10}$ e.s.u.

Boltzmann's constant, $k = 8·62 \times 10^{-5}$ eV/°K

Planck's constant, $h \phantom{,} = 4·13 \times 10^{-15}$ eV sec

| Temperature, °K: | 100 | 200 | 273 | 300 |
|---|---|---|---|---|
| $k$T, in eV: | 0·0086 | 0·0172 | 0·0234 | 0·0257 |

1 eV $= 1·602 \times 10^{-12}$ erg

$n_i$ for silicon at 300°K $= 1·3 \times 10^{10}$/cm³.

The nomograph overleaf *Figure A.1* is reproduced from the paper by Blankenship[1]. It is calculated from the following data:

$$\mu_n = 1,200 \text{ cm}^2/\text{V sec}; \ \mu_p = 450 \text{ cm}^2/\text{V sec}$$

$$\rho = 1/N.\mu \quad q = 6·25 \times 10^{18}/N.\mu \quad \Omega \text{cm}$$

$$\epsilon = 12$$

$$X^2 = 1·326 \times 10^7 \ V/N. \text{cm}^2; \text{ or } X = 3·64 \times 10^7 \ (V/N)^{\frac{1}{2}} \text{ microns}$$

$$C/\text{cm}^2 = 1·061 \times 10^4/X \quad \text{pF} \ (X \text{ is in microns})$$

159

# APPENDIX A

The dotted line shows the method of employing the nomograph, for a surface barrier (or $N$–$P$) detector in crystal of 3,600 $\Omega$cm. With 45 V reverse bias the barrier layer is 200 $\mu$, about the range of a 5 MeV

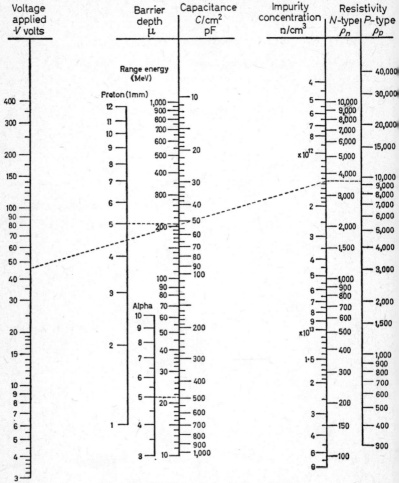

*Figure A.1. Nomograph for barrier layers in silicon*

proton. The capacitance is 52 pF/cm². Similar results are obtained for a $P$–$N$ junction in material of 9,500 $\Omega$cm.

*Figure A.2* is derived from Blankenship's nomograph[1]. The two entry scales (Volts and Impurity Concentration) are unchanged. The barrier depth scale is recalculated for $\epsilon = 16$. Values for mobilities assumed are stated below, and these were used for the resistivity scales. The capacitance equation is altered for the new value of $\epsilon$.

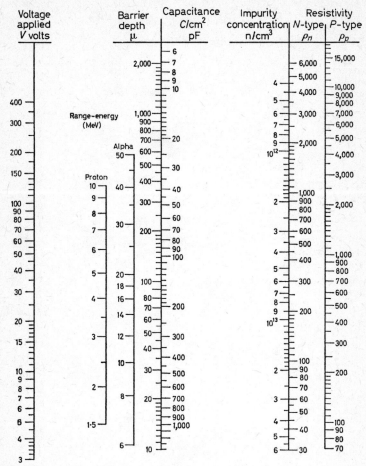

Figure A.2. Nomograph for barrier layers in germanium

Proton and $\alpha$-ranges were obtained from a nomograph due to R. R. Wilson[2].

$$\mu_n = 3{,}500 \text{ cm}^2/\text{V sec}; \; \mu_p = 1{,}500 \text{ cm}^2/\text{V sec}$$
$$\rho = 1/N.\mu \quad q = 6{\cdot}25 \times 10^{18}/N\mu \quad \Omega\,\text{cm}$$
$$\epsilon = 16$$
$$X^2 = 1{\cdot}77 \times 10^7 \; V/N. \; \text{cm}^2; \text{ or } X = 4{\cdot}21 \times 10^7 \; (V/N)^{\frac{1}{3}} \text{ microns}$$
$$C/\text{cm}^2 = 1{\cdot}416 \times 10^4/X \quad \text{pF} \; (X \text{ is in microns}).$$

## TABLE A.1. PROPERTIES OF SOME SEMICONDUCTORS

| Semiconductor | Energy gap $E_G$ | Drift mobilities† | | Highest atomic number $Z_m$ | Intrinsic resistivity $\rho_i$ | Minority carrier lifetime† | | Density | Dielectric constant $\epsilon$ |
| | | Electrons $\mu_n$ | Holes $\mu_p$ | | | P-type (electrons) $\tau_n$ | N-type (holes) $\tau_p$ | | |
| | V | cm²/V sec | | | Ω cm | sec | sec | g/cm³ | |
|---|---|---|---|---|---|---|---|---|---|
| Silicon | 1·08 | 1,300 | 500 | 14 | $3 \times 10^5$ | $10^{-3}$ | $10^{-3}$ | 2·33 | 11·7 |
| Germanium at 300°K | 0·66 | 3,800 | 1,800 | 32 | 47 | $10^{-3}$ | $10^{-3}$ | 5·32 | 15·7 |
| Germanium at 77°K | 0·75 | 10,000 | 15,000 | 32 | $5 \times 10^4$ | | $10^{-3}$ | | 15·0 |
| Gallium antimonide | 0·67 | 4,000 | 650 | 51 | 0·09 | $<10^{-6}$ | $<10^{-6}$ | 5·62 | |
| Gallium phosphide | 2·25 | 110 | 75 | 31 | | $<10^{-8}$ | $<10^{-8}$ | | |
| Gallium arsenide | 1·39 | 8,500 | 1,000 | 33 | | | $7 \times 10^{-7}$ | 5·3 | 12·5 |
| Indium antimonide | 0·18 | 78,000 | 750 | 51 | | $<10^{-6}$ | $<10^{-6}$ | 5·77 | 17 |
| Indium phosphide | 1·29 | 4,600 | 650 | 49 | | | $6 \times 10^{-8}$ | 4·79 | 14 |
| Indium arsenide | 0·36 | 33,000 | 460 | 49 | | | $<10^{-6}$ | | 14 |
| Aluminium antimonide | 1·65 | 200 | 420 | 51 | | | | 4·22 | 11 |
| Lead sulphide | 0·37 | 400 | 600 | 82 | | $<10^{-6}$ | | 7·60 | 22·5 |
| Lead selenide | 0·26 | 1,000 | 900 | 82 | | $2 \times 10^{-5}$ | | 8·15 | 20·5 |
| Selenium | 1·75 | 1 | 1 | 34 | | | | 4·79 | 8·5 |
| Zinc oxide | 3·2 | 1,000 | | 30 | | | | 5·66 | 8·1 |
| Titanium oxide | 3·0 | 1 | 1 | 22 | | | $10^{-8}$ | 4·20 | 8·4 |

NOTES (1) All figures quoted are for 300°K except where otherwise stated, and are in many cases approximate
(2) †The figures are roughly representative of the best reported experimental results
(3) A useful reference for numerical data is *Constantes Sélectionnés Relatives Aux Semiconducteurs*, Pergamon Press, 1961

The resistivity scales refer to 300° K. The calculation, starting from the impurity concentration scale, is only valid over temperature ranges for which complete ionization of the impurity centres may be assumed, but this is approximately true, even down to about 80° K.

## DATA ON SEMICONDUCTORS

The table on p. 162 gives some figures on semiconductor materials collected from various sources. It was found on attempting to compile these data that sources sometimes disagreed to a considerable extent. This is not surprising in view of the great variations which occur from sample to sample and the difficulty of carrying out accurate measurements of such properties as carrier lifetime, drift mobility, and even resistivity, in semiconductor crystals. With the exception of the figures quoted for silicon and germanium the data should be accepted with some reserve.

## REFERENCES

[1] BLANKENSHIP, J. L. and BORKOWSKI, C. J., *Proceedings of the Seventh Scintillation Counter Symposium*, Inst. Radio Engrs, N.Y., N.S.7, Nos. 2 and 3 (Sept. 1960) p. 190
[2] SEGRÉ, E. (Ed.), *Experimental Nuclear Physics*, Vol. 1, Wiley, New York (1953)

# APPENDIX B

## CARRIER LIEFTIME AND DIFFUSION LENGTH

### Carrier Lifetime

Let $n$ carriers move under diffusion for a short time, $dt$ and let $dn$ of them be caught by traps in this interval. Then, assuming homogeneous crystal,

$$\frac{dn}{n} \propto dt$$

Put

$$\frac{dn}{n} = \frac{dt}{\tau} \qquad \ldots (B1)$$

where $\tau$ is a constant of proportionality having the dimensions of time. Now let $n_0$ carriers reach the conduction or valence band simultaneously at time $t = 0$ and let their lives be $t_1, t_2, t_3, \ldots, t_n$ respectively. Let $n(t)$ be the number still surviving at time $t$. Then, during the period $t$,

$$\frac{dn}{n(t)} = \frac{-dt}{\tau} \qquad \ldots (B1a)$$

Integrating,

$$n(t) = n_0 e^{-t/\tau} \qquad \ldots (B2)$$

so there is an exponential distribution of lifetimes.

The mean lifetime, $\bar{t}$ is

$$t = \frac{1}{n_0} \int_0^\infty n \, . \, dt = \int_0^\infty e^{-t/\tau} \, . \, dt = \tau \qquad \ldots (B3)$$

Therefore the constant of proportionality which satisfies (1) is the mean lifetime.

Under equilibrium conditions, with $n$ carriers per unit volume, the generation rate, $g$, is equal to the trapping rate, but of opposite sign. From eqn. (B1a)

$$g = \frac{-dn}{dt} = \frac{n}{\tau} \qquad \ldots (B4)$$

where $\tau$ is the carrier lifetime.

### Diffusion Length

The diffusion length is the average distance in any specified direction which a carrier will traverse by diffusion during its lifetime.

Its value has been determined from theory by Einstein and is found to be

$$L = \sqrt{(D.\tau)} \qquad \ldots \text{(B5)}$$

where $D$ is the diffusion coefficient. By another relationship due to Einstein,

$$D = \frac{kT}{q}.\mu \qquad \ldots \text{(B6)}$$

From (B5) and (B6),

$$L^2 = \frac{kT}{q}\mu\tau \qquad \ldots \text{(B7)}$$

*Relaxation Time*

Let a sample of semiconductor crystal be given, at time $t = 0$, an increment of one type of carrier, so that the concentration is $n_0$ as compared with the equilibrium concentration, $n_1$. It is assumed that $n_0$ is uniform over the whole sample. Then

$$\frac{dn}{dt} = \text{rate of creation of carriers} - \text{rate of extinction}$$

$$= \frac{n_1}{\tau} - \frac{n}{\tau} = -\frac{(n-n_1)}{\tau} \quad \text{(by eqn. (B1))}$$

The solution of this is

$$n = n_1 + (n_0 - n_1)\,e^{-t/\tau} \qquad \ldots \text{(B8)}$$

The relaxation time is the period taken by the system to reduce the excess concentration to a value $1/e$ times the initial value; in this simple case it is equal to the carrier lifetime, as shown by eqn. (B8).

The argument above is based on the assumption that the carrier lifetime remains constant. This would not be true in the case of a large transient.

# APPENDIX C

*The Depletion Layer*

The depth of the depletion layer can be calculated on the basis of a simplified theory which gives results of reasonable accuracy despite gross assumptions. These assumptions are that:

(*a*) the barrier is a region containing no carriers at all,
(*b*) the junction is abrupt.
(*c*) outside the barrier $n = N_D$, $p = N_A$, i.e. all impurity centres are ionized and the barrier has abrupt edges,
(*d*) $N_A$ and $N_D$ are uniform over the $P$ and $N$ regions respectively.

Let $x_n$ be the barrier width on the $N$ side and $x_p$ the width on the $P$ side of the junction, respectively. Let the total barrier width be $X = x_n + x_p$, where $x_n$ and $x_p$ are the charged zones.

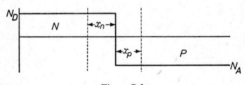

*Figure C.1*

From the fact that the charges are equal,

$$qN_D x_n = qN_A x_p$$

Therefore

$$x_n = \frac{x_p N_A}{N_D}$$

Therefore

$$x_n + x_p = X = x_p\left(\frac{N_A}{N_D} + 1\right) = x_p\frac{(N_A + N_D)}{N_D}$$

Similarly,

$$x_n + x_p = x_n\frac{(N_A + N_D)}{N_A}$$

166

Therefore

$$x_n + x_p = X = \frac{1}{2}\frac{(N_A + N_D)}{N_A N_D}(x_n N_D + x_p N_A) \qquad \ldots (C1)$$

The capacitance of a capacitor is given by:

$$C = \frac{\epsilon}{4\pi d} \quad \text{per unit area}$$

where $\epsilon$ is the dielectric constant and $d$ is the distance between the plates. In this case the charges are treated as if they were concentrated in the centre of each charge zone, i.e., at

$$\frac{x_n}{2} \quad \text{and} \quad \frac{x_p}{2}$$

respectively.

Therefore

$$d = \frac{X}{2}$$

and

$$C = \frac{\epsilon}{2\pi X}$$

But, $C = Q/V$ also, where $Q$ is the charge in each zone and $V$ is the height of the potential barrier (this is the small p.d. which arises under equilibrium conditions, plus the increase due to the applied bias). Substituting,

$$\frac{\epsilon V}{2\pi X} = Q \qquad \ldots (C2)$$

Now

$$Q = q N_D x_n = q N_A x_p$$

that is,

$$Q = \tfrac{1}{2}q(x_n N_D + x_p N_A) \qquad \ldots (C3)$$

From eqns. C (1), (2) and (3),

$$X = \frac{N_A + N_D}{N_A N_D}\cdot\frac{Q}{q} = \frac{\epsilon V}{2\pi q X}\cdot\frac{N_A + N_D}{N_A N_D}$$

Therefore,

$$X = \left(\frac{\epsilon V}{2\pi q}\cdot\frac{N_A + N_D}{N_A N_D}\right)^{\frac{1}{2}} \qquad \ldots (C4)$$

In the case of a surface barrier, where $N_D \gg N_A$,

$$X = \left(\frac{\epsilon V}{2\pi q N_A}\right)^{\frac{1}{2}} \qquad \ldots \text{(C5)}$$

and the barrier is, for practical purposes, entirely in the $P$ region.

### The Drift Current, $I_s$

This component of the reverse current is due to the diffusion of minority carriers from each side of the barrier into the depletion zone, where they come under the influence of the field and are carried across the barrier. Consider a cylindrical volume of the crystal, extending from the boundary of the depletion zone into the $P$ region. In any

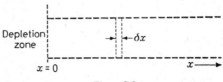

*Figure C.2*

small element, $\delta x$, of this cylinder the rate of electron generation, per unit volume, is $n_0/\tau_n$, where $n_0$ is the electron concentration and $\tau_n$ the minority carrier lifetime (i.e. the electron lifetime) in the bulk $P$ material, [see Appendix B, eqn. (4)]. The rate of disappearance of electrons depends on their local concentration and is given by $n/\tau_n$. The net rate of generation is, therefore,

$$\frac{n_0 - n}{\tau_n}$$

This must be balanced by an increased flow of electrons (from right to left in the diagram) across the boundary at $x$, as compared with that across the boundary at $x + \delta x$. The rate of flow is determined by the diffusion coefficient, $D_n$ and the balance in the equilibrium condition is given[1] by

$$\frac{-D_n \partial^2 n}{\partial x^2} = \frac{n_0 - n}{\tau_n}$$

Remembering that $L_n = \sqrt{(D_n \tau_n)}$, this differential equation is

$$\frac{\partial^2 n}{\partial x^2} - \frac{n}{L_n^2} = -\frac{n_0}{L_n^2}$$

and the steady state solution is

$$n = n_0 \left(1 - e^{-x/L_n}\right) \qquad \ldots \text{(C6)}$$

From this, the concentration gradient at the edge of the depletion zone, where $x = $ zero is

$$\left(\frac{\partial n}{\partial x}\right)_{x=0} = \frac{n_0}{L_n}$$

and the rate of flow per unit cross-section is

$$\frac{D_n n_0}{L_n}$$

Substituting for $D_n$, the drift current due to electrons from the $P$ side is

$$I_{s.p} = q \cdot \frac{L_n \cdot n_0}{\tau_n}$$

per unit cross-section, and the total drift current density is

$$I_s = q\left(\frac{L_n \cdot n_0}{\tau_n} + \frac{L_p p_0}{\tau_p}\right) \qquad \ldots \text{(C7)}$$

Now, $$L^2 = D\tau = \frac{kT}{q} \cdot \mu \cdot \tau \quad \text{(eqn. B7)}$$

therefore

$$\frac{L}{\tau} = \frac{\mu^{\frac{1}{2}}}{\tau^{\frac{1}{2}}} \sqrt{\left(\frac{kT}{q}\right)} \qquad \ldots \text{(C8)}$$

Also, if $p$ is the hole concentration on the $P$ side

$$n_0 p = n_i^2$$

therefore,

$$n_0 = \frac{n_i^2}{p} \qquad \ldots \text{(C9a)}$$

Similarly,

$$p_0 = \frac{n_i^2}{n} \qquad \ldots \text{(C9b)}$$

Substituting (C9) and (C8) into (C7) gives

$$I_s = q^{\frac{1}{2}} n_i^2 \sqrt{(kT)} \left(\frac{\mu_n^{\frac{1}{2}}}{p \cdot \tau_n^{\frac{1}{2}}} + \frac{\mu_p^{\frac{1}{2}}}{n \tau_p^{\frac{1}{2}}}\right) \qquad \ldots \text{(C10a)}$$

Further, if $\rho_p$ is the specific resistance of the $P$ material, then

$$\sigma_p = \frac{1}{\rho_p} = q \cdot p \cdot \mu_p \quad \text{approximately,}$$

the contribution of the minority carriers being ignored.

Therefore

$$p = \frac{1}{q\rho_p \mu_p}$$

Substituting in (C10a)

$$I^s = q^{\frac{3}{2}} n_i^2 \sqrt{(\mu_n \mu_p . kT)} \left( \frac{\mu_p^{\frac{1}{2}} \rho_p}{\tau_n^{\frac{1}{2}}} + \frac{\mu_n^{\frac{1}{2}} \rho_n}{\tau_p^{\frac{1}{2}}} \right) \qquad \ldots \text{(C10b)}$$

This expresses the drift current directly in terms of the measurable properties of the bulk material.

In surface junctions, where the volume of crystal on one side of the junction is very small, it is usually assumed that there is no appreciable contribution of drift current from that side, and one of the terms in the above expression is neglected; for example, in a P–N junction detector the theoretical relationship is

$$I_s = q^{\frac{3}{2}} n_i^2 \mu_p . \rho_p \sqrt{\left( \frac{kT \mu_n}{\tau_n} \right)} \qquad \ldots \text{(C11)}$$

By simple algebraic methods it can be shown that eqn. (C10b) may be expressed in the alternative form,

$$I_s = \frac{b}{(1+b)^2} . \frac{kT}{q} . \sigma_i^2 \left( \frac{1}{\sigma_n L_p} + \frac{1}{\sigma_p L_n} \right) \qquad \ldots \text{(C12)}$$

where $b = \mu_n / \mu_p$ and $L_p$, $L_n$ are the diffusion lengths of the minority carriers on the $N$ and $P$ sides respectively.

### The Generation Current, $I_G'$

This component of reverse current is due to the generation of carriers in the depletion zone itself, these being collected by the field across the barrier independently of diffusion processes. The current therefore depends on the volume of the depletion zone and increases (according to a half-power law) with the applied bias. It is to be expected that the generation rate will differ in the two parts of the zone, where the basic crystal has vastly different properties. However, it is usual to neglect the contribution of the surface film (the $N$ layer in a P–N detector) and assume a constant value for the generation rate over the whole zone. The current density is then

$$I_G' = q . g . X \qquad \ldots \text{(C13)}$$

Substituting for $X$,

$$I_G' = g \sqrt{\left( \frac{\epsilon q V}{2\pi N_A} \right)} \qquad \ldots \text{(C14)}$$

A theoretical assessment of the generation rate in the depletion zone is difficult but Sah *et al.*[2] conclude that, in the bulk material,

$$\frac{n_i}{2\tau} < g < \frac{n_i}{\tau} \qquad \ldots (C15)$$

where $\tau$ is the minority carrier lifetime in the same material outside the zone. It is usual to assume that $g = n_i/\tau$.

It is further assumed that the parent material has all its acceptors (or donors in the case of an *N–P* junction) fully ionized, so that $N_A = P$, and this is expressed in terms of resistivity and mobility by the equation

$$N_A = p = \frac{1}{q\rho_p\mu_p}$$

Making the substitution from this and from eqn. (C15) gives

$$I'_G = \frac{q \cdot n_i}{\tau}\left(\frac{\epsilon\rho_p\mu_pV}{8\pi}\right)^{\frac{1}{2}} \qquad \ldots (C16)$$

## *Practical Units*

McKenzie and Waugh[3] give the following relationships for the bulk reverse current in silicon at ambient temperatures: $\rho$ is in $\Omega$cm, $V$ in volts and $\tau$ in microsecs. In each case the first term is the drift current and the second is the generation current.

For a *P–N* junction, in high resistivity *P*-type crystal,

$$I_r = 1\cdot7 \times 10^{-2}\frac{\rho}{\tau^{\frac{1}{2}}} + 38\rho^{\frac{1}{2}}\frac{V^{\frac{1}{2}}}{\tau} \quad \text{m}\mu\text{A/cm}^2 \qquad \ldots (C17)$$

For an *N–P* junction

$$I_r = 4\cdot7 \times 10^{-2}\frac{\rho}{\tau^{\frac{1}{2}}} + 64\rho^{\frac{1}{2}}\frac{V^{\frac{1}{2}}}{\tau} \quad \text{m}\mu\text{A/cm}^2 \qquad \ldots (C18)$$

The ratio of generation current to drift current is, by these expressions, approximately

$$2 \times 10^3\left(\frac{V}{\rho\tau}\right)^{\frac{1}{2}}$$

Choosing a fairly typical case, $V = 100$ V, $p = 3,000$ $\Omega$cm, $\tau = 10^{-4}$ sec (100 $\mu$sec), shows the generation component to be greater by a factor of 40. Assuming the same lifetime with $V = 10$ V and $\rho = 12,000$ $\Omega$cm gives a ratio of about 6. Therefore, in general, the generation current is substantially greater, but this may no longer be true in the future if it becomes possible to obtain crystal having higher resistivity and lifetime.

## The Surface Leakage Current

No mathematical treatment of practical use in connexion with detectors is possible for the surface leakage current. For average crystal geometry and good surface conditions it appears to be of the same order as the bulk reverse current. Moisture, and some other adulterants on the surface can increase it by several orders of magnitude [4]. The surface leakage obeys, very approximately, an ohmic law and is therefore less under low bias.

## REFERENCES

[1] DUNLAP, W. C., *An Introduction to Semiconductors*, Wiley, New York (1957) p. 153

[2] SAH, C. T., NOYCE, R. N. and SHOCKLEY, W., *Proc. Inst. Radio Engrs*, N.Y. 45 (1957) 1228

[3] McKENZIE, J. M. and WAUGH, J. B. S., *Proceedings of the Seventh Scintillation Counter Symposium*, Inst. Radio Engrs, N.Y., N.S.7, Nos. 2 and 3 (Sept. 1960)

[4] VAN DER ZIEL, A., *Fluctuation Phenomena in Semiconductors*, Butterworths, London (1959) p. 142

# APPENDIX D

## Particle Spectrometry by Pulse Height Analysis

A BRIEF description is given of the general method of particle spectrometry when using a detector with a linear response to energy. If, as is usually the case, the detector receives mono-energetic groups of particles the amplifier output is a series of pulses whose heights are grouped in narrow zones, each zone corresponding to the energy of

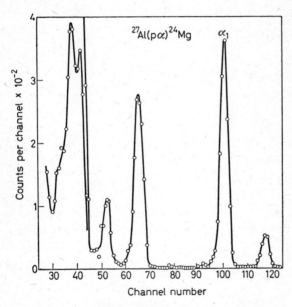

*Figure D.1. α-particle spectrum obtained by using a semiconductor detector*

(D. A. Bromley, *Semiconductor Nuclear Particle Detectors*, Nat. Acad. Sci. (Washington), Publ. 871, p. 72)

one component of the flux. For spectrometry the amplifier is connected to a pulse height analyser, which selects pulses according to their heights and feeds the signals to a finite number of counting channels. It is common to employ an analyser with up to 512 channels

173

and these may be pre-set to cover the required range of pulse height, all pulses of height above and below this range being rejected.

After operating for a suitable time, the counts recorded in each channel are plotted against the channel number, giving the sort of result shown in *Figure D.1*. The plotting, in fact, is usually done electronically and the spectrum displayed on a cathode ray tube. Channel numbers are proportional to particle energy and the position of a peak therefore shows the energy of the particle concerned. The height of the peak is proportional to the intensity of that particular radiation.

In the example of *Figure D.1* that part of the spectrum below channel 43 was recorded in a shorter period of time than the upper part, as it would otherwise have been largely off the scale.

The virtue of any particular system of particle spectrometry is measured by the ability to distinguish particles having nearly the same energy and by the ability to recognize as two separate events the receipt of two particles at nearly the same time.

## Energy Resolution

This is primarily determined by the width of the peak shown in the spectrum and arises from the statistical variation in the pulse heights, as recorded, from nominally mono-energetic particles. The obvious figure of merit is the standard deviation of pulse height, in units of electron volts. The variance is also used, when considering the effects of electrical noise or the separate contributions of known sources of error. The figure of merit most employed is the width of the peak, as it appears on the spectrum, measured at half its height. In such cases a system is said to give an energy resolution for the particles concerned of '$X$.keV (f.w.h.m.) at $Y$.MeV', or as appropriate. The abbreviation 'f.w.h.m.' means 'full width half maximum'. A resolution so defined needs to be related to the energy of the particles concerned and it is therefore, common practice to express the width at half height as a percentage of the energy recorded. In this case the statement would be '$X$.per cent (f.w.h.m.) at $Y$. MeV'.

Deficiencies in resolution arise from many causes other than in-consistencies in the counter employed. Source or target thickness, and collimation problems, are examples affecting the distribution in true particle energy at the detector, and further statistical variations arise from electrical noise in the amplifier and analyser. To separate the contribution of the detector from that of the rest of the system is a very laborious task, not often attempted. Where resolution figures are quoted in the text of this study it can only be said that the detector is capable of giving resolution at least as good as the figure quoted.

## Time Resolution

The obvious figure of merit in this case is the smallest time interval which can occur between pulses that are recognized and counted as separate pulses. The detector characteristic most relevant to the problem of obtaining good time resolution is the pulse rise time, usually measured as the interval during which the pulse rises from 10 per cent to 90 per cent of its full height. For rise times exceeding about $10^{-7}$ sec the detector determines the resolving time which, with good electronics, will be substantially less than the rise time. With exceptionally fast detectors it becomes increasingly difficult to analyse and record the pulses at a speed which will realize the full time resolution of which the detector itself is capable, particularly if the amplifier input signal is a small one.

# INDEX

Series resistance, 58, 71, 153
Side entry, 118
Silver chloride, 27
Space charge, 23, 25, 124
   detector, 44
   junction, at a, 50, 55, 59, 81
   trapping, 23, 36, 40
Spectrometry, 94, 110, 113, 173
Stability, 27, 85, 114
Stacked detectors, 119
Statistics, carriers, of, 90
Substitutional impurity, 6
Surface,
   barrier, 56
      detectors, 56, 80
   effects, 25, 85
   flicker noise, 41
   leakage current, 25, 66, 72, 74, 172
   protection, 75, 85
   trapping, 26

Temperature,
   effects, 31, 72, 86, 93, 117, 126, 157
      carrier concentration, on, 5, 10, 13
         mobility, on, 15, 86
         conductivity, on, 16
Thermal noise, 40
Thin detectors, 99, 103, 146
Time,
   constant, 34, 136, 138, 152
   resolution, 45, 68, 71, 99, 136, 152, 175

Total absorption peak, 110
Total energy peak, 111
Transient effects, 22, 165
Transistor detector, 118
Trap, 19
Trapping, 19
   generation, recombination, 22
   scatter, 22
   space charge, 23, 36, 40
Tritons, 61
Tube,
   flicker noise, 138
   shot noise, 139

Uranium, 110
Units, 159, 171

Valence band, 4, 10, 12
Vaporization in vacuo, 36, 82, 85, 145

Window, 68, 85, 117
   P.I.N. detector, in a, 128, 147
Work function, 143

Zinc sulphide, 27
Zone refining, 38